HEALTH AND MEDICAL ECONOMICS

ECONOMICS INFORMATION GUIDE SERIES

Series Editor: Robert W. Haseltine, Associate Professor of Economics,
State University College of Arts and Science at Geneseo, Geneseo, New York

Also in this series:

HISTORY OF ECONOMIC ANALYSIS—*Edited by William K. Hutchinson*

RUSSIAN ECONOMIC HISTORY—*Edited by Daniel and Vera Kazmer*

THE ECONOMICS OF MINORITIES—*Edited by Kenneth L. Gagala*

ECONOMIC EDUCATION—*Edited by Catherine Hughes*

TRANSPORTATION ECONOMICS—*Edited by James P. Rakowski*

LABOR ECONOMICS—*Edited by Ross E. Azevedo**

ECONOMIC HISTORY OF CANADA—*Edited by Trevor J.O. Dick **

MATHEMATICAL ECONOMICS AND OPERATIONS RESEARCH—
*Edited by Joseph Zaremba**

MONEY, BANKING, AND MACROECONOMICS—*Edited by James M. Rock*

INTERNATIONAL TRADE—*Edited by Ahmed M. El-Dersh**

ECONOMIC DEVELOPMENT—*Edited by Thomas A. Bieler**

SOVIET-TYPE ECONOMIC SYSTEMS—*Edited by Z. Edward O'Relley**

AMERICAN ECONOMIC HISTORY—*Edited by William K. Hutchinson**

URBAN ECONOMICS—*Edited by Jean Shackleford**

REGIONAL ECONOMICS—*Edited by Jean Shackleford**

ECONOMIC HISTORY OF ASIA—*Edited by Molly K.S.C. Lee**

*in preparation

The above series is part of the
GALE INFORMATION GUIDE LIBRARY

The Library consists of a number of separate series of guides covering
major areas in the social sciences, humanities, and current affairs.

General Editor: Paul Wasserman, Professor and former Dean, School of
Library and Information Services, University of Maryland

Managing Editor: Dedria Bryfonski, Gale Research Company

HEALTH AND MEDICAL ECONOMICS

A GUIDE TO INFORMATION SOURCES

Volume 7 in the Economics Information Guide Series

Ted J. Ackroyd

Assistant Professor of Health Planning and Administration
College of Human Development
Pennsylvania State University

Gale Research Company
Book Tower, Detroit, Michigan 48226

Library of Congress Cataloging in Publication Data

Ackroyd, Ted J
  Health and medical economics.

  (Economics information guide series ; v. 7)
(Gale information guide library)
    1. Medical economics--Bibliography. 2. Med-
ical economics--Abstracts. I. Title.
Z6675.E2A27 [RA410] 016.3384'7'3621 73-17567
ISBN 0-8103-1390-1

. . . TO MY WIFE, MY CHILDREN
AND MY PARENTS

VITA

Ted J. Ackroyd is assistant professor of health planning and administration at the College of Human Development, Pennsylvania State University. He received his B.A. magnum cum laude from the State University of New York at Geneseo in economics; his M.A. in economics and Ph.D. in hospital and health administration/health economics from the University of Iowa. He pursues an integrated research program comprised of health planning and administration, social forecasting, and regionalization of health facilities/services.

Ackroyd is also involved in medical group practice administration, where he is directing a nonprofit corporation concerned with the provision of services to the medically indigent and directing the transition to a fully computerized management information system.

CONTENTS

ACKNOWLEDGMENT

The courteous, efficient, and extremely accurate work of Mrs. Nancy Hopkins-- friend and typist--is acknowledged with sincere appreciation.

PREFACE

This is not a typical reference text; it provides more than a mere compilation of sources in health and medical economics. The entire text represents a laboratory for the demonstration of a unique reference system--one which truly facilitates and enhances the research process. This system, which is set forth in chapter 1, eliminates the need for a standard subject index. The reader is referred to Appendix A for the location of an entry by author. A second distinguishing feature relates to the character of the entry annotations in this reference system. In general, these were intentionally made quite lengthy, providing the user of this volume with a significant level of information both at the initial phase of and throughout a research project. Instead of the typical generalities, specific textual abstractions (e.g., empirical results) are provided. Reading all or a majority of the annotations in each chapter would at least familiarize the user with most of the currently popular and some of the less popular concerns in health and medical economics.

Regarding the scope of this reference text, several matters should be noted. First, the authors referenced in this text are economists. While many persons contribute to the literature on health and medical economics, the contributions are frequently from a noneconomic perspective. The importance of such contributions is recognized, but consistency with the entire Economics Information Guide Series of the Gale Information Guide Library required that only the literature written by economists be compiled. (The reader will find the volume of literature by economists to be quantitatively significant.)

A second aspect of the scope of this text is that most entries were written no earlier than 1960. Health and medical economics began to emerge as an independent area of investigation in the early 1960s. In his foreword to the significant work on hospital costs by Ingbar and Taylor (1968), John T. Dunlop observed:

> Indeed, a field of medical economics has at last emerged, built upon an appreciation of the distinctive features of medical care institutions and the insightful application of the tools of economic theory and the analysis of mountains of quantitative data through statistical and econometric procedures, including the use of computers.

(Note, however, that some authors included in this text were quite actively involved in the health field prior to 1960, e.g., Fein, Fuchs, Garbarino, Ginzberg, Klarman, and Mushkin.)

Finally, the contents of this volume are merely representative. The text is representative of both the authors and the subject matter--not all authors or minor subject areas have been included. Basically, a system was developed and applied; through this system, it is hoped that the research process is facilitated and enhanced, and that a good subject/author representation has evolved.

Chapter 1

A SYSTEMATIC REFERENCE TEXT

In this introductory chapter, a "search and retrieval" reference system will be explained. The rationale for developing a systematic reference text is set forth in the first section (A). The second part provides a detailed explanation of the reference system, including the construction of the system (B.1), the development of a search and retrieval mechanism (B.2), and a discussion of entry format in this system. The chapter concludes with a reference matrix (section C) containing all the entries annotated in the subsequent chapters.* By the end of this chapter, the researcher will have learned to use the matrix.

A. RATIONALE FOR DEVELOPING A REFERENCE SYSTEM

There is a large and continually growing body of literature written by economists in the area of health and medical economics. In order to facilitate meaningful research, a framework to organize this literature is necessary. Thus, to provide a means for organizing current and future literature, a unique reference system was developed. The remainder of chapter 1 will explain this system and how to use it.

B. DEVELOPMENT AND USE OF THE REFERENCE SYSTEM

(B.1) Elements of the Reference Matrix

The process of entry collection was structured according to a combined health-medical sector and economics framework. The skeleton of this framework, or matrix, is provided on the next page; subsequently, this skeleton is expanded and filled in with entry reference numbers in the full matrix of section C.

Entries included in this reference text fit into one or more of the <u>cells</u> within

---

*The nine entries of section 6.C are not referenced according to the matrix system.

1

MATRIX FRAMEWORK

Sector	1 Consumption of Services	2	Provision of Services 3 L	4 PK	5 F	6 HK	7 PK	8 FK
(1) Short-Term General Hospitals								
(2) Physician Office Practice								
(3) Health Insurance								
(4) Public Health								
(5) Disease/Illness Specific								
(6) International Health								
(G) General and Misc. Health /Medical								

where: L - labor   in the   HK - human capital   exclusive
        PK - physical capital   provision   PK - physical capital   of service
        F - fiscal matters   of services   FK - financial capital   provision

2

this matrix--cells are formed by the intersection of matrix rows and columns. To understand what any one cell means, it is necessary to first discuss the rows and columns. These (rows/columns) constitute the combined health-medical sector and economics frameworks.

The matrix rows (left side of page) numerically identify health/medical sectors; row (1), for example, represents the short-term general hospital sector. These sectors are the health/medical subject areas about which economists have written and continue to write, and they represent a basic level of organization in the evolving reference system. The titles and subtitles of chapters 2-6--those chapters containing the annotated references--are the health/medical sectors identified here as matrix rows. At the most basic level, then, this reference system organizes studies according to the general health/medical subject areas examined by economists. The areas included are (1) short-term general hospitals (chapter 2); (2) physician office practice (chapter 3); (3) health insurance (chapter 4); (4) public health, disease/illness-specific analyses, and international health (chapter 5); and (5) general and miscellaneous health/medical sector studies (chapter 6).**

There are eight columns in the matrix, and these are organized in an economics framework. The columns, then represent a second means for organizing studies in health and medical economics. When these are combined with the health/medical sectors (rows), a matrix framework is formed. Column organization conforms to basic elements of economics in that consumption and provision (demand and supply) of health services as well as the resource categories (human capital, physical capital, and financial capital) are included as means for categorizing studies. Definitions and the structure of these columns are given next to provide a basic understanding of the economic framework used in entry classification.

> Columns 1, 2, 3, 4, and 5 refer to the consumption and provision of health services.
>
>> Column 1 represents the consumption of health services.
>>
>> Column 2 represents a general level for the provision of health services.
>>
>> Columns 3, 4, and 5 divide the process of service provision into: labor (column 3), physical capital (column 4), and fiscal matters (column 5) as these relate to the provision of services.
>
> Columns 6, 7, and 8 identify the traditional resource divisions used in economics, but here they are separated from the subject of service provision. These three columns are, then, distinguished from columns 3, 4, and 5 as follows: The resources of human capital,

---

**It should be noted that this list is not comprehensive. The areas identified do constitute, however, the primary emphasis of economists since 1960. Additions to the list are anticipated as new areas develop and as more intensive analysis of currently "less popular" subject areas occurs (e.g., mental health).

physical capital, and/or financial capital can, in themselves, be the primary subject of analysis without having explicit reference to the provision of services (which derives from using these inputs in the production process). Thus, in these three columns, the process of service provision is secondary to the primary resource emphasis, whereas in columns 3, 4, and 5, the specific context is that of service provision.

These eight columns form the economics framework for the classification of the entries in this text. Each of the studies included is located and described according to combined health/medical sector and economics frameworks. Together, these frameworks constitute a matrix in which, again, the intersection of any row with any column yields a matrix cell. Each cell, therefore, represents a "mini" health/ medical sector and economics framework; the entries numerically identified in each cell (see section C) are said to refer to that particular "mini" framework. The next section uses this intersection concept as a basis for organizing the search and retrieval procedures.

(B.2) The Search and Retrieval Processes

In order to search for text entries that will constitute a reference list for a particular subject area, intersections need to be generated. Basically, the user specifies his/her research interest(s), asking, in effect, what type(s) of references may be needed. Two sample research specifications, or mini frameworks, are derived below:

I. Research interest - provision of services [column 2] in the short-term general hospital sector [row 1].

    Interpretation - the intersection of column 2 and row 1 is specified; a cell is formed.

II. Research interest - the role of labor [column 3] in the provision of services in the short-term general hospital sector [row 1].

    Interpretation - the intersection of column 3 and row 1 is specified; again, a cell is formed.

Specifying areas of interest--i.e., generating intersections--assures the subsequent retrieval of relevant sources. After identification of the search base(s), retrieval simply requires that the appropriate cell(s) be checked, thereby allowing the formation of a numerical reference list. To illustrate, consider mini framework II above--the role of labor in the provision of short-term general hospital services. Using the Reference Matrix provided on pages 7-9 in section C of this chapter yields a numerical reference list having seven cell entries: [1.19, 1.24, 1.25, 1.31, 1.38, 1.53, 1.58]. Entry retrieval would then proceed according to the "numerical directions" of this list: To explain the numerical directions, let us look at cell 1.19. The number to the left of the decimal point refers to a matrix row in the framework. In this case, the 1 represents the short-term general hospital. The number to the right of the decimal, 19, indicates the nineteenth annotation in the chapter on short-term general

4

hospitals (chapter 2). This cell has thus led the researcher to an annotation of Martin Feldstein, "Hospital Cost..." Thus, entries* [19, 24, 25, 31, 38, 53, 58] are described as emphasizing the role of labor in the provision of short-term general hospital services. This list of references provides relevant research material according to the search base specified (labor's role in sector 1). Checking the appropriate cell yielded seven references which specifically examine this subject area. Similarly, other reference lists could be generated for any search combination specified by the researcher.

It should also be noted that nonsector-specific research interests can also be accommodated--here, in two ways. First, chapter 6 contains references (designated by a G) that are not specific to any particular health/medical sector (with the exception of entries __.57 through __.68. References here are specific to service consumption, service provision, and/or the resource categories (HK, PK, FK), but they are not specific to any one sector. For example, a discussion of service provision need not relate to any one sector or small group of sectors; instead, it could simply emphasize the provision of services in general. These nonsector-specific references (the "G's") comprise most of chapter 6.

A second means for accommodating nonsector-specific research interests is to formulate the following search command: Compile a list of all text entries which examine, e.g., the resource identified as physical capital (PK, column 7). No intersection is here specified; a row or group of rows is not designated. Retrieval would simply require listing all references in the PK column (7) for the entire Reference Matrix. Thus, entries 1.7, 1.18, 1.46, 1.47, 1.51, 1.66, 1.69, 2.23, 3.6, 6.4, G.22, and G.47, __.64 would comprise this list. The researcher could then read the annotations in the various chapters and use these as relevant research sources.

(B.3) Explanation of Entry Format

Text entries are presented according to a specific format. First, the entry reference number and full bibliographic citation are provided. Each entry is then described in at least two, and frequently three, ways; these three descriptive means are designated as levels A, B, and C.

Level A is presented in symbolic notation. Letters are used to designate the matrix columns (i.e., the economics framework) to which the reference relates. The basic symbolic list includes:

C_C^S - consumption of services (column 1)
P_S^S - provision of services (column 2)
$P_S^S L$ - the role of labor in service provision (column 3)
$P^S PK$ - the role of physical capital in service provision (column 4)

*The entries are also alphabetically ordered in each chapter or chapter subdivision.

$P^S F$ – fiscal matters in service provision (column 5)
HK, PK, FK – resource categories (columns 6, 7, and 8)

Any combination of these entry descriptors can appear on level A. The intent here is simply to provide a "picture" of what is contained in each reference. *direct quote*

Level B contains the annotation, abstracted from the original work.

Level C is used as a descriptor only when appropriate; it is an attempt to identify an important characteristic of the entry or what tool(s) may be needed to comprehend the entry. "Empirical" is a frequently used descriptor; the researcher is thus informed that a significant level of empirical information is reported in the study. "Quantitative methods" is another frequently used descriptor, informing the researcher that an understanding of the methods is needed to assure effective use of the study.

Finally, note that a "See also" section is often provided below an entry--further references are cited therein. Thus, the annotated list of entries (ordered alphabetically in Appendix A) is enlarged by a significant number of additional references listed in the "See also" segments.

C. REFERENCE MATRIX

The following pages contain the reference matrix which has been systematically explained in section (B) of this chapter. To derive maximum benefit from this text, the researcher is encouraged to become familiar with the very simple search and retrieval procedures set forth in section (B). These procedures are summarized as follows:

(1) SEARCH

    A. Define health/medical framework being researched by using the sectors (rows)

    B. Define economics framework (columns)

    C. The intersection of levels A and B specifies the search cells, where the health/medical and economics frameworks intersect. (For the "no intersection" alternative, see section B.2)

(2) RETRIEVAL

    A. List the entry numbers included in the specified cells

    B. Use these numbers to locate the corresponding text entries

SHORT-TERM GENERAL HOSPITALS

Sector	1 Consumption of Services	2 Provision of Services	3 L	4 PK	5 F	6 HK	7 PK	8 FK
(1)		1.1						
	1.2				1.2			
		1.3						
					1.4			
		1.5						
					1.6			
							1.7	1.7
	1.8	1.8						
				1.9	1.9			
					1.10			
					1.11			
					1.12			
					1.13			
					1.14			
	1.15				1.15			
						1.16		
	1.17	1.17						
	1.18						1.18	
	1.19		1.19		1.19			
	1.20				1.20			1.20
		1.21						
					1.22			
	1.23							1.23
			1.24					
			1.25		1.25			
					1.26			
		1.27						
	1.28	1.28						
					1.29			
					1.30			1.30

SHORT-TERM GENERAL HOSPITALS

SHORT-TERM GENERAL HOSPITALS

Sector	1 Consumption of Services	2 Provision of Services			6 HK	7 PK	8 FK
			3 L	4 PK	5 F			
(1)			1.31		1.31			
					1.32			
					1.33			
					1.34			
					1.35			
					1.36			
		1.37						
			1.38	1.38				
					1.39			
				1.40	1.40			
					1.41			
				1.42	1.42			
						1.43		
	1.44				1.44			
	1.45			1.45				
							1.46	
							1.47	1.47
		1.48						
	1.49							
	1.50	1.50						1.50
							1.51	
		1.52						1.52
			1.53		1.53			
		1.54						
					1.55			
				1.56				
					1.57			
			1.58		1.58			
	1.59							
	1.60	1.60						

(Sector label, rotated: SHORT-TERM GENERAL HOSPITALS)

SHORT-TERM GENERAL HOSPITALS

Sector	1 Consumption of Services	2 Provision	of	Services	6	7	8
			3 L	4 PK	5 F	HK	PK	FK
(1)	1.61			1.61				
	1.62							
				1.63	1.63			
					1.64			
		1.65						
							1.66	
		1.67						
	1.68	1.68						1.68
						1.69	1.69	
						1.70		

(Sector column label: Short-Term General Hospitals)

Chapter 3

PHYSICIAN OFFICE PRACTICE

Sector	1 Consumption of Services	2 Provision	of	Services		6	7	8
			3 L	4 PK	5 F	HK	PK	FK
(2)								
			2.1					
			2.2					
						2.3		
	2.4		2.4		2.4			
	2.5	2.5						
					2.6			
	2.7	2.7						
			2.8		2.8			
			2.9					
			2.10		2.10			
					2.11			
					2.12			
						2.13		
					2.14			
	2.15				2.15			
			2.16		2.16			
Physician Office Practice		2.17						
	2.18							
	2.19	2.19						2.19
			2.20					
						2.21		
					2.22			
							2.23	
			2.24		2.24			
						2.25		
			2.26					

HEALTH INSURANCE

Sector	1 Consumption of Services	2 Provision	of Services			6	7	8
			3 L	4 PK	5 F	HK	PK	FK
(3)	3.1							
	3.2		3.2					
		3.3						
								3.4
								3.5
	3.6					3.6	3.6	
	3.7				3.7			3.7
								3.8
					3.9			
						3.10		3.10
	3.11	3.11						
								3.12
	3.13							3.13
	3.14	3.14						
					3.15			3.15
					3.16			
								3.17
								3.18
	3.19							3.19
	3.20							3.20
		3.21						3.21
	3.22							
	3.23							
					3.24			
	3.25	3.25						3.25
	3.26	3.26						

Health Insurance

11

Chapter 5
PUBLIC HEALTH, DISEASE/ILLNESS-SPECIFIC ANALYSES, INTERNATIONAL HEALTH

Sector	1 Consumption of Services	2 Provision of		Services	6	7	8
			3 L	4 PK	5 F	HK	PK	FK
(4) Public Health	4.1 4.2 4.4 4.5 4.7 4.9	4.1 4.2 4.4 4.5 4.6 4.7 4.8 4.9 4.10				4.3 4.11		4.9
(5) Disease/Illness-Specific	5.5	5.8		5.2	5.1 5.2 5.3 5.4 5.6	5.9		5.7
(6) International Health	6.1 6.3 6.5 6.6	6.3 6.6 6.7	6.1			6.2 6.4 6.8	6.4	6.4

GENERAL AND MISCELLANEOUS HEALTH/MEDICAL SECTOR STUDIES

Sector	1 Consumption of Services	2 Provision	of	Services	6	7	8
		3 L	4 PK	5 F	HK	PK	FK
(G)					G.1		
	G.2						
	G.3						
	G.4	G.4					
	G.5	G.5					
	G.6						
				G.7			
					G.8		
					G.9		
					G.10		
					G.11		
General Health and Medical		G.12					
		G.13					
	G.14	G.14					
	G.15	G.15					
	G.16	G.16					
					G.17		G.17
	G.18		G.18				
	G.19	G.19			G.19		
					G.20		
	G.21						
	G.22	G.22				G.22	
		G.23					
	G.24	G.24					
	G.25	G.25					
					G.26		
	G.27	G.27					
	G.28						
					G.29		
					G.30		

GENERAL AND MISCELLANEOUS HEALTH/MEDICAL SECTOR STUDIES

Sector	1 Consumption of Services	2 Provision of Services	3 L	4 PK	5 F	6 HK	7 PK	8 FK
(G)						G.31		
						G.32		
	G.33	G.33						
	G.34							
	G.35							
						G.36		
	G.37							
								G.38
	G.39	G.39						
						G.40		
						G.41		
	G.42							
					G.43			
	G.44							G.44
	G.45	G.45						
		G.46						
		G.47				G.47	G.47	
	G.48							
								G.49
	G.50							
	G.51							
		G.52						
	G.53	G.53						
								G.54
	G.55							
						G.56		
	_.57	_.57						
Minor Subject Areas				_.58	_.58			
	_.59	_.59						
	_.60							_.60

Sector: General Health and Medical

Chapter 6

GENERAL AND MISCELLANEOUS HEALTH/MEDICAL SECTOR STUDIES

Sector	1 Consumption of Services	2	Provision	of	Services	6	7	8
			3 L	4 PK	5 F	HK	PK	FK
Minor Subject Areas	_.62 _.63 _.66 _.67	_.62 _.63 _.67	 _.65	 _.68	 _.65 _.68	_.61 _.64	_.64	_.64

Chapter 2

SHORT-TERM GENERAL HOSPITALS

1.1 Ackroyd, Ted J. "Spatial Interaction Vectors: A Method for Examining the Spatial Distribution of Services among Non-Federal, Short-Term, General Hospitals." Doctoral dissertation, University of Iowa, 1974.

A. P^S

B. This original study uses the language of set theory to develop a methodology for analyzing the distribution of services among hospitals. The theoretical investigation utilizes and integrates microeconomics and regional economics through the generation of spatial interaction vectors--vectors which summarize and quantify elements of interaction that derive from the condition of spatial coexistence among hospitals.

C. Theoretical, methodological.

1.2 Baron, David P. "A Study of Hospital Cost Inflation." JOURNAL OF HUMAN RESOURCES (Winter 1974): 33-49. *No volume*

A. C^S, $P^S F$

B. "The objective of this study is the estimation of the amount of hospital cost inflation associated with increases in factor prices, technological and case-mix change, and growth in hospital demand....The specification of the cost function is [here] based on the neoclassical microeconomic theory of production in which a hospital is assumed to minimize the cost of satisfying an exogenous demand for hospital care."

Two output measures are developed for the analysis, a patient-days adjusted measure and a cases-treated measure. "The estimates indicate that the majority of the increase in average costs for the sampled hospitals was associated with factor price increases [nursing labor hours, ancillary labor hours, professional labor hours, general labor hours, administrative labor hours, and capacity], while changes in technology and/or case mix also resulted in significant cost increases. These increases were offset to a relatively minor extent by the cost effects of increases in hospital output. To the extent that improvements

17

in the quality of care are reflected by the observed increases
in full-time equivalent employees per bed, the costs due to
changes in technology and/or case mix may reflect the cost of
quality improvements."

C. Empirical, quantitative methods

1.3   Berki, Sylvester E.   HOSPITAL ECONOMICS.   Lexington, Mass.:   D.C.
Heath and Co., 1972.   270 p.

A. P^S

B. Berki attempts to provide "a framework for the analysis of
the operations of short-term general (acute) hospitals..."
Primary emphasis is given to hospital production processes.
"...the understanding of [hospital] objectives, functions,
and contributions, the understanding of its economic bases of
operations, is prerequisite to the formulation of policies to assure that all Americans...can best benefit from the medical services our technology and resources can provide."   Topics discussed include:

(1) development of an analytic framework which stresses
the multiplicity of demands facing the hospital
(2) hospital objectives as derived from patients, physicians,
administrators, researchers, teaching units, and communi-
ties
(3) operational definitions of outputs
(4) productivity, costs, and efficiency, emphasizing the
issues of scale economies and efficiency
(5) the concepts of utilization and demand
(6) pricing and reimbursement as they relate to production
efficiency
(7) special problems of municipal hospitals

1.4   Berry, Ralph E., Jr.   "Cost and Efficiency in the Production of Hospital
Services."   HEALTH AND SOCIETY (formerly MILBANK MEMORIAL FUND
QUARTERLY) 52 (Summer 1974):   291-313.

A. $P^S F$

B. "This paper summarizes the general findings of a research
effort designed to complete a detailed analysis to identify and
measure the effects of factors which significantly affect the
cost and efficiency of the short-term general hospital system
in the United States."

A model which expresses hospital cost as a function of the
level of output, the quality of services provided, the scope of
services provided, factor prices, and relative efficiency was
empirically tested in approximately 6,000 hospitals for 1965-
67.   "The statistical analysis does provide insight to the factors affecting hospital cost: hospital services are produced subject to economies of scale but the absolute magnitudes are

rather insignificant; on the basis of the exceedingly limited data available it can be concluded that quality does affect costs; medical education is a significant factor affecting hospital costs; and product mix has a significant affect [sic] on costs. Three separate analyses are summarized specific to the product mix difference aspect of the production of hospital services, its affect [sic] on hospital cost analysis, and techniques that can be employed to account for product mix. Finally, an analysis of the characteristics of high cost and low cost hospitals is summarized."

C. Empirical, quantitative methods

1.5 _____. "On Grouping Hospitals for Economic Analysis." INQUIRY 10 (December 1973): 5-12.

A. P^S

B. An empirical attempt is made to determine if there is a systematic pattern in the availability of facilities and services in short-term general hospitals. Further, once such a pattern is ascertained, it is used to derive additional insight regarding the general nature of product mix and its impact on the provision of hospital services. Categories for empirical analysis include: types of hospital ownership; bed capacity; and service grouping--basic, quality-enhancing, complex, community, and special.

C. Empirical

1.6 _____. "Product Heterogeniety and Hospital Cost Analysis." INQUIRY 7 (March 1970): 67-75.

A. $P^S F$

B. "The essence of explaining variations in the cost of producing hospital services lies in understanding why hospitals might be operating at different points on the same cost curve [involves variations in output levels] and, more significantly, why hospitals might be operating on different cost curves [involves, e.g., quality, product mix, factor prices, efficiency]."

These two levels might well be interdependent. Furthermore, Berry observes that the basic model utilized in hospital cost research should include as categories of independent variables: level of output, quality of services, product mix (complexity of scope of services), factor prices, and efficiency. His concern is the treatment of variations in product mix as a determinant of variations in hospital service cost. To this end, forty variables related to product mix were subjected to factor analysis. "Eight common factors were generated that explained approximately 60 percent of the variation in the 40 variables used to represent product mix."

C. Empirical, quantitative methods

1.7   Brinker, Paul A., and Walker, Burley. "The Hill-Burton Act: 1948-1954."
       REVIEW OF ECONOMICS AND STATISTICS 44 (May 1962): 208-12.

       A. PK, FK

       B. A brief history of the Hill-Burton Act is provided in the
       introduction to this article. Included are the general purposes
       of the act and the two types of grants provided (one for sur-
       veys on hospital need and another for construction). Formulas
       for the allocation of grant money are then examined, as is the
       mechanism for state-level implementation (i.e., the state plan)
       of such funds. The second part of the article provides an em-
       pirical evaluation of the early Hill-Burton years, 1948-54. It
       was found that: (1) The percent of need-met ratio improved
       from 59 percent to 73 percent, though not all of this improve-
       ment was attributable to funds from this act. (2) Fulfilling one
       of its major purposes, the act, via its formulas, did result in
       larger per capita money sums being allotted to and spent by
       the lower income states. (3) "Lastly, the comprehensive plan-
       ning required of each state put hospital construction under sys-
       temization for the first time in the history of our country. In
       the two states studied, Oklahoma and Alabama, a preponder-
       ance of projects were located in rural areas where lack of
       facilities was greatest."

1.8   Carr, W. John. "Economic Efficiency in the Allocation of Hospital Re-
       sources: Central Planning vs. Evolutionary Development." In EMPIRICAL
       STUDIES IN HEALTH ECONOMICS, edited by Herbert Klarman, pp. 195-
       221. Baltimore: Johns Hopkins Press, 1970.

       Blind ref.

       For annotation see 6.59.

1.9   Carr, W. John, and Feldstein, Paul J. "The Relationship of Cost to Hos-
       pital Size." INQUIRY 4 (June 1967): 45-65.

       A. P^{S}PK, F

       B. "The primary purpose of this study [was] to estimate the net,
       or independent, effect of hospital size upon the cost of pro-
       viding care. The results indicate that, other things being
       held approximately equal, average cost per patient day falls
       initially as size is increased because of the economies associa-
       ted with the use of specialized personnel and equipment and
       then probably rises at very large size levels due to increased
       managerial problems of communication and control. Apparently,
       the greater the capability of a hospital to provide a wide
       range of diversified services, the more rapidly average cost
       initially falls with increased size."

       Multiple regression analysis was applied to 1963 data on 3,147
       U.S. voluntary short-term general hospitals, using these vari-
       ables: total cost, hospital size, number of services provided,
       number of outpatient visits, whether the hospital had a nursing

school, number of student nurses, number of different types of internship and residency programs, number of interns and residents, whether the hospital was affiliated with a medical school, and average wage rate.

1.10 Cohen, Harold A. "Hospital Cost Curves with Emphasis on Measuring Patient Care Output." In EMPIRICAL STUDIES IN HEALTH ECONOMICS, edited by Herbert Klarman, pp. 279-93. Baltimore: Johns Hopkins Press, 1970.

A. $P^S F$

B. Cohen attempts to develop a partial measure of hospital output in order to construct long-run hospital cost curves. The specific partial measure relates to the patient care segment of hospital output and involves a weighting of intermediate services. [See "Comment" by Paul J. Feldstein, 294-96.]

C. Empirical, quantitative methods

1.11 _____. "Variations in Cost among Hospitals of Different Sizes." SOUTHERN ECONOMIC JOURNAL 33 (January 1967): 355-66.

A. $P^S F$

B. Two aspects of cost variation with respect to hospital size among general, short-term hospitals are examined. One aspect relates to salary and wage differentials due to factors other than hospital size. A second area refers to the adjustment of hospital output measurement (patient days) according to the use and availability of auxiliary services. Studies comparing the costs of hospitals of different sizes have generally incorporated at least one of two biases in that they have failed to properly account for one or more of the aspects noted above. Cohen attempted to remove these biases by developing an adjusted total cost formula to account for differences in starting salary, and adapting the Saathoff and Kurtz measure of an adjusted patient day. Despite the (acknowledged) limited empirical base of this study, it is concluded that "the achievement [herein] of putting hospital data, both cost inputs and outputs of services, on a more comparable basis may facilitate wise planning and meaningful cost comparisons."

C. Empirical, quantitative methods

1.12 Collins, Gavin L. "Cost Analysis and Efficiency Measures for Hospitals." INQUIRY 5 (June 1968): 50-61.

A. $P^S F$

B. This study emphasizes the need for developing universal cost data which reflect hospital efficiencies. Such data would provide a base for equitable rate setting, intra-hospital and inter-hospital efficiency comparisons, and development of future hospital systems which can deliver a given amount of high quality medical care at a minimum cost. Currently, these three objectives cannot generally be realized because of the volume effect, allocation effects, the complexity-of-service effect, and the output-composition effect—obstacles which derive from existing deficient cost accounting procedures. A cost accounting methodology is suggested which would provide a base for both equitable rate setting and intra- and inter-hospital efficiency comparisons.

C. Empirical

1.13 Davis, Karen. "Relationship of Hospital Prices to Costs." APPLIED ECO-NOMICS 3 (June 1971): 115-25.

A. $P^S F$

B. The author notes: "Even though the belief that hospitals set prices equal to average costs is widespread, little empirical evidence has been obtained on the validity of this assumption." The purpose of this paper is to examine the ratio of hospital prices to average costs. Three hypotheses are considered: (1) The price-average cost ratio is a constant; (2) The price-average cost ratio is a function of the "need for additional investment"; and (3) The price-average cost ratio is a function of demand and supply conditions. To test these hypotheses, cross-section regressions are developed for all fifty states, using 1960-69 data. Empirical evidence here "contradicts the prevailing view that hospitals merely attempt to recover costs in their pricing policies. In addition, the view that the excess of price over average cost is merely an attempt on the part of the hospital to accumulate sufficient revenue to make needed investment is not substantiated. Instead, price-average cost ratios are found to be sensitive to certain demand and supply conditions."

C. Empirical, quantitative methods

1.14 _____. "Theories of Hospital Inflation: Some Empirical Evidence." JOURNAL OF HUMAN RESOURCES 8 (Spring 1973): 181-201.

A. $P^S F$

B. "This article examines three alternative hypotheses of hospital inflation: the demand-pull hypothesis, [the] cost-plus reimbursement hypothesis, and the labor cost-push hypothesis. The theoretical foundation of the cost-reimbursement hypothesis is explored:...under either the profit-maximization or quantity-maximization hypothesis, hospitals will not have an incentive to increase costs unless the percentage of patients covered by the cost-plus reimbursement scheme exceeds about 95 percent (for a 5 percent cost-plus factor). At present, hospitals are unlikely to have cost-reimbursement patients in that range. The empirical results lead to a rejection of the hypothesis that hospital costs increase with the extensiveness of cost reimbursement within the range observed....The growth of cost-reimbursement schemes was similarly not important in explaining hospital wage rates....A significant upward shift in hospital costs and hospital wages in the Medicare period, however, was obtained."

C. Empirical, quantitative methods.

1.15 Davis, Karen, and Russell, Louise B. "The Substitution of Hospital Outpatient Care for Inpatient Care." REVIEW OF ECONOMICS AND STATISTICS 54 (May 1972): 109-20.

A. C^S, $P^S F$

B. Properties of the demand for hospital outpatient care are first investigated. "In order to explore the possibility of inducing the substitution of outpatient for inpatient care, the model to be investigated must specify fully all the means, including prices, by which substitution might be induced. A demand function for outpatient visits is estimated by regresssion methods using data on 48 states for the year 1969....The estimates provide striking evidence of the responsiveness of outpatient visits to prices: the elasticity of outpatient visits demanded with respect to outpatient price is highly significant ‑|.0; its cross-elasticity with respect to inpatient price is also significant and varies from 0.85 to 1.46, depending on the measure used." The authors also estimate the demand for inpatient care in order to "permit a fuller exploration of the substitution between outpatient and inpatient care." Possible implications of these elasticities for the total costs of hospital care are also examined.

C. Empirical, quantitative methods

1.16 Ehrenberg, Ronald G. "Organizational Control and the Economic Efficiency of Hospitals." JOURNAL OF HUMAN RESOURCES 9 (Winter 1974): 21-32.

A. HK

B. "This paper presents estimates of the determinants of hospitals' demand for registered nurses (RNs) and licensed practical nurses (LPNs) utilizing a cross-section sample of over 2,000 hospitals. Of primary interest is the degree to which hospitals substitute across different classes of nurses as their relative wages change and whether the degree of substitution is related either to the type of organization controlling a hospital or to the size of a hospital. [It was empirically suggested that] the substitution does not appear to occur uniformly across different bed-size classes and that the response appears nonsymmetric, in the sense that full‑time equivalent employment levels of

each type of nurse are responsive primarily to the category wage
and not to the wage level of the alternative nursing class.
The asymmetry of responses may imply that technical inefficiency rather than factor substitution is occurring....The results
for state and local government hospitals differ from those for
private hospitals. In the main, nursing employment levels in
the publicly operated hospitals seem to be insensitive to the
wages of different categories of nurses....Our estimates suggest
that substitution is technically and legally possible and may be
occurring currently, if only for particular control types and
sizes of hospitals."

C. Empirical, quantitative methods

1.17 Feldstein, Martin S. "An Aggregate Planning Model of the Health Care
Sector." MEDICAL CARE 5 (November/December 1967): 369-81.

For annotation see G.62. *B hid arof.*

1.18 _____. "Hospital Bed Scarcity: An Analysis of the Effects of Inter-
Regional Differences." ECONOMICA 32 (November 1965): 393-409.

A. C^S, PK

B. "This article is an example of the use of economic analysis
in studying the operation of health care systems." The specific area of inquiry is "the effects of area differences in the
scarcity of hospital beds on the way in which these beds are
used." Although the 1960 empirical data are from the United
Kingdom, the type of economic analysis used, the empirical
base of fifteen natural service areas, and the findings have
applicability to the United States. A responsiveness index is
used to estimate responsiveness values so that the sensitivity
of bed use to scarcity is measured. It is found that "the number of cases treated is substantially more responsive to differences in bed scarcity than is the mean stay per case....This
finding will of course have implications for the problems of
planning hospital bed supply. In particular, it casts serious
doubts on the current attempts to evaluate the number of beds
that 'should' be provided in an area by the current demands
for beds....[Furthermore], differences in bed scarcity are not
merely absorbed by variation in 'slack' capacity. The effect
of greater relative scarcity is to reduce the number of hospital beds used per thousand population."

C. Empirical

1.19 _____. "Hospital Cost Inflation: A Study of Nonprofit Price Dynamics."
AMERICAN ECONOMIC REVIEW 61 (December 1971): 853-72.

A. C^S, P^SL, F

B. An empirically estimable model of the nonprofit hospital industry is presented and used to analyze the problem of hospital cost inflation. The model "emphasizes the basic causes of hospital cost inflation through time and of hospital cost variation among different areas. The analysis suggests that, despite the nonprofit nature of the hospital industry, hospital cost inflation can be explained by a model of dynamic price adjustment to excess demand....The source of inflation is the pressure of the rising demand induced by increases in insurance coverage, personal incomes, the availability of hospital oriented specialists, etc....Rapidly increasing wages and the expansion of hospital employment can be viewed primarily as the results rather than the fundamental causes of this inflation." A twelve-equation behavioral model of hospital inpatient services is developed; then the demand and price adjustment equations are estimated using a pooled cross-section of time series for individual states, 1958-67.

C. Empirical, quantitative methods

1.20 _____. "The Welfare Loss of Excess Health Insurance." JOURNAL OF POLITICAL ECONOMY 81 (March/April 1973): 251-80.

For annotation see 3.7.

1.21 Greenfield, Harry I. HOSPITAL EFFICIENCY AND PUBLIC POLICY. New York: Frederick A. Praeger, Publishers, 1973. 80 p.

A. P^S

B. "What the present work has attempted to do has been to look at hospitals that are at the core of the health system alternately through micro- and macroeconomic lenses. Our aim has been to bring into focus economic factors influencing the kind of health care that hospitals are actually delivering and to indicate how public policy might be applied at nodal points to elevate existing to higher levels of care, i.e., health services that are qualitatively superior, more accessible, and produced with greater efficiency....[This] has not been an exercise in cost-benefit analysis. It has been designed rather to draw attention to larger problems in the economics of hospital care and to provide a rationale and framework for subsequent application of cost-benefit or other decision-guidance approaches to specific features of organizational alternatives. Our microeconomic view...[emphasizes]...that the conventional economic analysis of the firm can shed a good deal of light on the operations of the contemporary hospital. In particular, while the 'firm' itself is 'nonprofit,' utilizing customary economic incentives for its employees should be increasingly relied upon to achieve efficiency. We have examined the hospital's production function...by bringing costs into our viewing field. The effect of supply-demand interrelations on hospital output, or occupancy rate, have been considered along with further discussion of the nature of hospital output and productivity. This led us into more refined definitions of input and output and of the calculation of what appear to us to be new measures of hospital output and productivity. Given our findings ...we proceeded to focus on the potentials for and some techniques of intrahospital efficiency. Emphasis was placed on physical and functional reorganization as well as on the use of reimbursement as a tool for change. Our macroeconomic lens focused on systemic, i.e., interhospital problems. Finally, we advocated a policy of governmental supervision--not ownership and control--utilizing a public utility rate-setting mechanism combined with a federal health system modelled after the Federal Reserve System for over-all coordination and direction."

1.22 Hill, Daniel B., and Stewart, David A. "Proprietary Hospitals Versus Nonprofit Hospitals: A Matched Sample Analysis in California." BLUE CROSS REPORTS r.s. 9 (March 1973): 10-16.

A. $P^S F$

B. "The study reported herein demonstrates a methodology for developing data for comparative analyses of proprietary and nonprofit hospitals." Using bed size and geographic location (California) as their basis for developing a sample data set, the following preliminary (and not to be assumed "generalizable") results were reported: "Data on the provision and utilization of nursery facilities, the relationship between total expenses and hospital size and the provision of profitable facilities supported the hypothesis that proprietary hospitals are more oriented toward profit maximization than are nonprofit hospitals. Data on inpatient utilization, total expenses, and unprofitable facilities did not support the hypothesis, but rather, reflected a picture of similarities between the two types of hospitals. The profit maximization hypothesis, to the extent that it is supported, leads to several general policy implications. The behavior of proprietary hospitals will clash with the demands of social priorities in the health field...to the extent that these priorities are inconsistent with the relative profitability of alternative modes of hospital operations. If these are inconsistent, then either 1) proprietary hospitals must be regulated and required to meet standards of performance consistent with social priorities, or 2) pricing and reimbursement structures for hospital services must be changed to make profitable modes of operation consistent with social priorities."

C. Empirical

1.23 Hill, Daniel B., and Veney, James E. "Kansas Blue Cross/Blue Shield Outpatient Benefits Experiment." MEDICAL CARE 8 (March/April 1970): 143-58.

For annotation see 3.13.

1.24 Hurd, Richard W. "Equilibrium Vacancies in a Labor Market Dominated by Non-Profit Firms: The 'Shortage' of Nurses." REVIEW OF ECONOMICS AND STATISTICS 55 (May 1973): 234-40.

A. P^SL

B. "First, a model of hospital input utilization is presented, viewing hospitals as maximizers of a welfare function representing the goals of hospital management. With the aid of this model it is demonstrated that under a wide range of behavioral assumptions monopsony hospital employers will report vacancies in equilibrium. Second, the monopsony question is put to an empirical test in a multiple regression setting. A significant negative relationship is demonstrated between the wages of nurses and concentration in the hospital sector. This result indicates that where monopsony power is present in the market for nurses, that power will be exploited. The conclusion follows that the high vacancy rates for nursing positions result in part from an oligopsonistic market structure."

C. Empirical, quantitative methods

1.25 Ingbar, Mary Lee, with Lee, Sidney S. "Economic Analysis as a Tool of Program Evaluation: Costs in a Home Care Program." In THE ECONOMICS OF HEALTH AND MEDICAL CARE, Proceedings of a conference held May 1962, Ann Arbor, Mich., edited by S.J. Axelrod, pp. 173-210. Ann Arbor: University of Michigan Press, 1964.

A. P^SL, F

B. "This paper uses the Home Care program of the Beth Israel Hospital (BIH), Boston, to illustrate how the statistical and conceptual techniques of economic analysis can arm the administrator of a program with foreknowledge of the implications of action. By applying these methods, decisions relating to which patients should be admitted, which services provided, what personnel utilized, and what prices charged can be made against a setting of factual prediction. Consequently, in choosing among feasible courses of action and in selecting between those individual social goals which conflict, administrators can be fully cognizant of the consequences of decisions upon the effectiveness of the program as a whole. In the first part of this paper, the issues involved in defining the costs of coordinated home care are discussed. The definitions developed are then applied to the BIH program in subsequent sections. As methods are elaborated in the third section, they are applied to the BIH program in order to delineate the considerations involved in predicting and controlling costs and in pricing services. The final section discusses the implications of the findings for the evaluation of programs of medical care."

C. Empirical

1.26 Ingbar, Mary L[ee]., and Taylor, Lester D. HOSPITAL COSTS IN MASSA-
CHUSETTS. Cambridge, Mass.: Harvard University Press, 1968. 237 p.

A. $P^{S}F$

B. This study attempts to develop a more detailed knowledge
of the cost structure of the hospital industry. The authors emphasize that understanding the behavior of hospital costs will
help to improve methods for describing, comparing, predicting,
and controlling such costs. Econometric methods were applied
"to a large body of data on the operation of Massachusetts
hospitals in an effort to estimate the cost structure of the hospital industry in the Commonwealth." A secondary objective
was "to develop a method for efficiently organizing, coding,
analyzing, and interpreting cost information for the hospital
industry." The principal questions investigated were: "What
causes costs to vary among hospitals? Do they vary simply
because activity levels differ from hospital to hospital or is
there something more fundamental involved? How does hospital size enter the picture? Are larger hospitals really more
efficient than smaller hospitals in terms of lower costs per
patient day or per unit of service? What is the influence of
the occupancy rate on hospital costs? What is the effect, if
any, of the composition of services, that is, the product-mix?
Finally, are costs at the departmental level determined by the
same factors as costs at the aggregate level, and are there
any economies of scale at the departmental level?"

C. Empirical, quantitative methods

1.27 Jacobs, Philip. "A Survey of Economic Models of Hospitals." INQUIRY
11 (June 1974): 83-97.

A. P^{S}

B. In his introduction, the author divides economic models of
hospitals into two categories: (1) "organism" models--"those
that treat the hospital as an 'organism' or entity with its own
goals which are usually stated in terms of some aspect(s) of
performance, such as quantity and/or quality of output, profits
..."; and (2) "exchange" models--those which assume the hospital to be "an institution that facilitates exchange and/or en-
ables the individuals involved to attain their own goals." Organism models analyze a hospital's performance, whereas exchange models focus on the behavior of involved individuals
(viewing firm performance as a means to an end). Using this
categorical division, Jacobs identifies several points to be
examined in his subsequent survey of hospital economic models:
(1) The condition in nonprofit hospitals of policies being form-
ulated both by physicians and management--this condition requires examination of the physician's autonomy and the decision-
making process in the context of utility maximization. (2)
The quality of services is integral to economic models of hos-

pitals. (3) The forms of medical market structure represent yet another area of inquiry. The author concludes that: "In the first group [organism models], the emphasis on a 'mechanical' choice model which fits the institution has not been successful, probably because the analysts have not been clear about the nature of the institutions....Since the second group of models are more institutionally oriented, they perhaps yield greater gains at a time when institutional understanding is not great....[Parts] of the picture have been studied with greater consistency and deeper insight with these models."

C. Theoretical

1.28 Joseph, Hyman. "Hospital Insurance and Moral Hazard." JOURNAL OF HUMAN RESOURCES 7 (Spring 1972): 152-61.

For annotation see 3.14.

1.29 Joseph, Hyman, and Folland, Sherman. "Uncertainty and Hospital Costs." SOUTHERN ECONOMIC JOURNAL 39 (October 1972): 274-84.

A. P^SF

B. "Since the demand for hospital services has a stochastic element, the hospital planner must decide on the optimal hospital size in the face of uncertain demand. In this paper, uncertainty about the daily census of a hospital and how it affects the optimal size of the hospital is analyzed in a theoretical model, which suggests the empirical estimates that are present....This paper utilizes a theory of the behavior of hospital planners and data for 116 Iowa hospitals to estimate the reduction in the expected number of patients who would be turned away that is attributable to the last hospital bed. These results are then used to estimate the costs that are incurred by hospitals so that they may avoid turning away a patient. Finally, the costs that would be incurred to avoid turning away a patient are tabulated for rules about hospital size that are different from [those] indicated by Iowa data."

C. Empirical, quantitative methods

1.30 Kaitz, Edward M. PRICING POLICY AND COST BEHAVIOR IN THE HOSPITAL INDUSTRY. New York: Frederick A. Praeger, Publishers, 1968. 192 p.

A. P^SF, FK

B. "The focus of this study is an investigation of management behavior in the short-term general hospital industry. The financial decision-making process, particularly the cost-price relationship, was investigated, and this process was then related to the financial and accounting practices of the various third-party payment systems, especially the cost-based systems (Blue

Cross, Medicare, and Medicaid). This overview of managerial behavior was then related to the steady increase in hospital costs....In general, the study has shown that the cost-based, third-party payment system has, all other forces held constant, been a key force motivating the steady and inordinate increase in hospital costs in the past twenty years. It has helped to increase costs by removing a substantial portion of the business risk in hospital operations while failing to provide either an incentive for efficient production of medical care or a penalty for inefficient production." Included in the analysis were an examination of the operating characteristics of the industry, a review of the legislative and financial background of the third-party payment system, and an analysis of the decision-making process within a sample of Massachusetts hospitals.

1.31 Kessel, Reuben A. "Price Discrimination in Medicine." JOURNAL OF LAW AND ECONOMICS 1 (October 1958): 20-53.

For annotation see 2.10.

1.32 Klarman, Herbert E. "Approaches to Moderating the Increases in Medical Care Costs." MEDICAL CARE 7 (May/June 1969): 175-90.

A. $P^S F$

B. "It is suggested here that proposals for achieving reduced expenditures or moderation in the rate of increase be appraised in terms of current knowledge. With three types of problem areas taken as illustrations, different conclusions seem warranted. It is believed that the time has come to move to curtail the supply of hospital beds, in order to limit use. The current evidence on the effect of prepaid group practice is regarded as insufficiently sturdy to warrant an active policy of promotion. However, specific studies that promise early results are indicated. In the area of provider reimbursement, existing mechanisms are clearly deficient. A good deal of research is needed, as well as possibly experiments in diverse arrangements for payment."

C. Empirical

1.33 _____. "Increase in the Cost of Physician and Hospital Services." INQUIRY 7 (March 1970): 22-36.

A. $P^S F$

B. An empirical description is used as the base for developing an accounting framework. Specifically, there is a factual description of "the marked and persistent acceleration in this country of the increase in expenditures and prices (or unit cost) for physician and short-term hospital services against the background of their respective long-term trends...to the year 1929." An accounting framework is developed and applied in an effort to measure relative contributions of several factors to these increased expenditures.

C. Empirical

1.34 _____. "The Increased Cost of Hospital Care." In THE ECONOMICS OF HEALTH AND MEDICAL CARE, Proceedings of a conference held May 1962, Ann Arbor, Mich., edited by S.J. Axelrod, pp. 227-54. Ann Arbor: University of Michigan Press, 1964.

A. $P^S F$

B. "The objective of this paper is to examine the changes in hospital cost that have occurred in one large city [New York City], to analyze alternative explanations of the changes, and to point out some of the implications of the analysis. Better understanding of the factors governing changes in hospital cost will lead to improved estimates of the direction and slope of hospital cost in the future. [Further]...the study of hospital finances in a particular setting offers certain methodological advantages. It is possible to control the quality of data, with the result that differences and variations may be attributed to real factors with a greater degree of assurance than when nation-wide data are used. There is less need to make adjustments in order to compensate for ambiguities in definition or for the unrepresentative character of samples. The realism of the analysis can be further enhanced by making comparisons among groups of hospitals that have been classified according to meaningful criteria."

C. Empirical

1.35 Lave, Judith R., and Lave, Lester B. "Estimated Cost Functions for Pennsylvania Hospitals." INQUIRY 7 (June 1970): 3-14.

A. $P^S F$

B. First, the hospital cost literature is briefly reviewed. Then, the authors develop "a method of studying the changes in hospital costs which finesses the problems stemming from the multi-product nature of hospital output." Their basic model assumption is "...while there are output differences among hospitals, within a hospital, output is constant [i.e., a constant case mix] over a short period of time." They assume hospitals are characterized by a single cost function, and they pool data to estimate a cross-section, time series model. The estimated empirical results are then presented and compared for the two regions of analysis (greater Philadelphia and western Pennsylvania). These results demonstrate support for their model.

C. Empirical, quantitative methods

See also:

Lave, Judith R., and Lave, Lester B. "Hospital Cost Functions." AMERICAN ECONOMIC REVIEW 60 (June 1970): 379-95.

This article provides a more detailed account of their study.

1.36 Lave, Judith R.; Lave, Lester B.; and Silverman, Lester P. "A Proposal for Incentive Reimbursement for Hospitals." MEDICAL CARE 11 (March/April 1973): 79-90.

A. $P^S F$

B. "In the early 1960's, a number of observers argued that the current method of reimbursing hospitals by third parties would be a factor contributing to increasing hospital costs. In this report, [the authors] analyze one method of reimbursing hospitals [retrospective reimbursement]--[they] postulate and test a number of hypotheses about the nature of the incentives that are built into the program, and then propose an alternative way of reimbursing hospitals. It is argued that a prospective reimbursement formula be negotiated and developed that depends on two factors: 1. an agreed upon rate of general inflation, and 2. an estimated cost function which captures important aspects of the case-mix which accounts for differential costs across hospitals. The cost function is presented, and various aspects of the proposed formula are discussed."

See also:

Hellinger, Fred J. "A Comment on 'A Proposal for Incentive Reimbursement for Hospitals'." MEDICAL CARE 12 (February 1974): 186.

No further mention

1.37 Lee, Maw Lin. "A Conspicuous Production Theory of Hospital Behavior." SOUTHERN ECONOMIC JOURNAL 38 (July 1971): 48-58.

A. P^S

B. "In this paper, an alternative theory of hospital behavior is proposed. The theory is based on the propositions that the preferences of hospitals are interdependent and certain inputs are acquired for purposes other than to meet the ordinary requirement of production." It is assumed that hospital administrators attempt to maximize utility and that their utility functions include such variables as salary, prestige, security, power, and professional satisfaction. Implicitly, then, administrator utility functions relate to the status of the hospitals in which they serve; and, it should be noted, the drive for status has become a socially recognized goal among administrators. In fact, "...the competition for status among hospitals lies at the root of some of the fundamental economic problems facing the hospital industry today." The behavioral model proposed by Lee "assumes that, as a producer of health care, each hospital has a desired status (S*) and an actual status (S).

The basic hypothesis...is that a hospital attempts to minimize the gap between its desired status (S*) and its prevailing status (S)," subject to a budget constraint. Then, to complete the behavioral model, a desired input function is specified. This function is assumed to be determined by the sociological structure of the hospital sector. A concluding section compares Lee's theory with other theories of hospital behavior (described as being based on the assumptions of sales maximization, output and prestige maximization, short-run net revenue maximization, and profit maximization).

C. Theoretical

1.38 _____. "Theoretical Foundation of Hospital Planning." INQUIRY 11 (December 1974): 276-81.

A. $P^S L$, PK

B. "This paper presents the result of an analysis of one major source of inefficiency in hospital care organization and describes a procedure which can be used to reduce this inefficiency." Such inefficiency is characterized as an inappropriate factor combination resulting in the under-utilization of specialized inputs--or, "a combination of too large a quantity of specialized inputs relative to the complementary input of hospital beds." The combination of hospital growth and lack of service-provision coordination among hospitals during this growth is defined as basic to the existence of this inefficiency. Lee suggests that "organizational efficiency requires specialization in the provision of hospital care...a major departure from the traditional mode of hospital care delivery." The concept of factor proportionality in the theory of production is suggested as providing a sound theoretical foundation for hospital planning (specialized hospital care delivery system).

C. Theoretical

1.39 Lee, Maw Lin, and Wallace, Richard L. "Problems in Estimating Multiproduct Cost Functions: An Application to Hospitals." WESTERN ECONOMIC JOURNAL 11 (September 1973): 350-63.

A. $P^S F$

B. Using as their base the multiproduct nature of hospital output, the authors describe a model of hospital costs and empirically estimate the relationship between hospital average costs and case mix. In section 1, organizational characteristics of general hospitals are examined, through the development of a cost model, to show the manner in which product heterogeniety influences unit costs of operations. Section 2 sets forth the empirical measurement relating to the effects of case mix on hospital costs. In part, this section serves to illustrate two broad complicating factors relating to multi-product hospital factor analysis: (1) Given that production functions for each of the separate products are not identifiable, the importance of appropriate output classification is demonstrated. (2) The nonprofit status of hospitals complicates the estimation of cost functions because the assumption of cost minimization behavior is not necessarily valid. The authors conclude that: "The results of this empirical work illustrate the usefulness of systematically accounting for the multiproduct nature of hospital output."

See also:

Lee, Maw Lin, and Wallace, Richard L. "Classification of Diseases for Hospital Cost Analysis." INQUIRY 9 (June 1972): 69-72.

This reports research preliminary to the article subsequently published in the WESTERN ECONOMIC JOURNAL.

1.40 Long, Millard F. "Efficient Use of Hospitals." In THE ECONOMICS OF HEALTH AND MEDICAL CARE, Proceedings of a conference held May 1962, Ann Arbor, Mich., edited by S.J. Axelrod, pp. 211-26. Ann Arbor: University of Michigan Press, 1964.

A. P^{S}PK, F

B. The focal point of this study is "a question of supply arising from one particular attribute of the demand for hospital services--fluctuations over time." The occurence of such fluctuations (of peak and off-peak periods) requires increased investment in plant and equipment. This requirement is common to both electrical power companies and hospitals--power companies have solved this problem through the development of interconnected grids, and Long shows the efficiency of an analogous solution for hospitals. He advocates coordinated action, a centralized community directorate. In his first of two main sections, the author hypothesizes that "resources could be saved if instead of attempting to have sufficient beds to meet their peak demands, hospitals planned to be full on occasion and, when full, to make use of": (1) swing beds, (2) rescheduling elective admissions, (3) sending patients to another hospital, and/or (4) providing the required service in an out-patient clinic or sending the patient to a nonhospital facility. The hypothesis is tested and presented in the second section, using fourteen Pittsburgh hospitals for the 1959-60 period. "Of the 3,960 beds in these fourteen institutions, 279 beds...would have been rendered unnecessary had the policies outlined [see hypothesis and alternatives] been pursued. Or to give a slightly different interpretation to the results, greater flexibility would enable these hospitals to treat 7 percent more patients with existing facilities."

C. Empirical

1.41 Mann, Judith K., and Yett, Donald E. "The Analysis of Hospital Costs: A Review Article." JOURNAL OF BUSINESS 41 (January 1968): 191-202.

A. $P^S F$

B. Three empirical studies of hospital costs are reviewed in an attempt to clarify their apparently conflicting results. The studies are examined in terms of their differing institutional settings, methodologies, and policy implications. Subsequently, Mann and Yett present an alternative theoretical formulation of cost behavior. [The three studies are also included in this bibliography: (1) Carr and P.J. Feldstein, "The Relationship of Cost to Hospital Size"--entry 1.9; (2) M.S. Feldstein, ECONOMIC ANALYSIS FOR HEALTH SERVICE EFFICIENCY--entry 6.3; and (3) Ingbar and Taylor, HOSPITAL COSTS IN MASSACHUSETTS--entry 1.26.] Throughout this review, the importance of developing a consistent and definitive hospital cost model is stressed.

1.42 McCaffree, Kenneth M. "The Economic Basis for the Development of Community Mental Health Programs." MEDICAL CARE 6 (July/August 1968): 286-99.

For annotation see 5.2

1.43 McKersie, Robert B., and Brown, Montague. "Nonprofessional Hospital Workers and a Union Organizing Drive." QUARTERLY JOURNAL OF ECONOMICS 77 (August 1963): 372-404.

A. HK

B. Development of a behavioral model regarding union support/nonsupport was the essence of this study project. The study analyzed the impact of the unsuccessful 1959-60 organizing effort at Chicago's Mt. Sinai Hospital and "discusses the characteristics which distinguish the behavior of the nonprofessional workers who faced several important decisions [concerning] whether to join the union, whether to strike, and whether to picket." Bases for the analysis included differences in job-related factors, individual beliefs and values, and social factors.

C. Empirical, quantitative methods

1.44 Monsma, George N., Jr. "Marginal Revenue and the Demand for Physicians' Services." In EMPIRICAL STUDIES IN HEALTH ECONOMICS, edited by Herbert Klarman, pp. 145-60. Baltimore: Johns Hopkins Press, 1970.

For annotation see 2.15.

1.45 Morrill, Richard L., and Earickson, Robert. "Hospital Variation and

Patient Travel Distances." INQUIRY 5 (December 1968): 26-34.

A. C^S, P^SPK

B. This paper explores whether the pattern of distances that patients travel to hospitals varies according to the kind of hospital. Data were collected for 123 Chicago area hospitals on each of ninety-nine variables for which hospitals show meaningful variation--patient-handling capacity, quality and service variation, costs and means of payment, patient population characteristics, hospital service area characteristics, interhospital relations, changes over a period of time, occupancy, and length of stay. The emphasis in on the relation of hospital and patient, given the general purpose of studying hospital location. These ninety-nine variables were aggregated to form nine composite variables; thus, a grouping analysis was utilized, involving internal characteristics of hospitals and external characteristics of service areas. Distance decay functions were subsequently generated and examined for hospitals of varying size, level of care, and relative location (central, suburb, or satellite).

C. Empirical, quantitative methods

1.46 Muller, Charlotte F., and Worthington, Paul. "Factors Entering into Capital Decisions of Hospitals." In EMPIRICAL STUDIES IN HEALTH ECONOMICS, edited by Herbert Klarman, pp. 399-415. Baltimore: Johns Hopkins Press, 1970.

A. PK

B. Forty voluntary New York City hospitals and twenty-one years of data were used in an attempt to determine and examine factors which might systematically explain the investment decisions of voluntary hospitals. The basic hypothesis tested was that "an evaluation by the hospital of the productive contribution of alternative stocks of capital is a determinant of desired investment, and thus of the level of investment activity." (See "Comment" by Judith R. Lave and Robert M. Sigmond in EMPIRICAL STUDIES, pp. 416-19.)

C. Theoretical, empirical, quantitative methods

1.47 _____. "The Time Structure of Capital Formation: Design and Construction of Municipal Hospital Projects." INQUIRY 6 (June 1969): 42-52.

A. PK, FK

B. The concern of this study is "the time required to translate funds into facilities within the municipal hospital system of New York City. The provision for capital improvement...is made within...the capital budgeting process and the capital improvement construction process. Three aggregate financial flows trace out the consequences of these processes: the annual departmental requests, the amount of annual adoptions for the department in the capital budget, and the annual amounts expended for actual progress achieved--work performed or materials supplied." Design activity in construction is singled out for special attention, and it is found that: "1) it will take as long to design a project as it will to build it, and 2) larger projects will economize on time per dollar of project value. But the primary source of this economy will be in construction, not in design."

C. Empirical

1.48 Newhouse, Joseph P. "Toward a Theory of Non-Profit Institutions: An Economic Model of a Hospital." AMERICAN ECONOMIC REVIEW 60 (March 1970): 64-74.

A. P^S

B. "In this paper a very simple model of a hospital is developed, and its implications are considered at some length. [It is] concerned with the relationship between a hospital's non-profit status and economic efficiency." To understand that relationship, a maximand for the hospital decision-maker is postulated. Elements of this maximand are the quantity and quality of services provided, where both are here viewed as variables of choice. Quality is measured by a vector of characteristics; quantity, by the number of patient days. Decisions relating to these elements derive collectively from administrators, trustees, and the medical staff. Since these quantity/quality decisions are subject to a budget constraint, Newhouse actually postulates a constrained quantity-quality maximization. Based on this model, it is concluded that the non-profit status of voluntary hospitals may cause misallocation of resources because: "First, there is a bias against producing lower quality products (a bias in the sense that a profit-maximizing firm would produce such qualities). Second, there is little reason to think that a non-profit hospital will enter in response to a profitable opportunity....Philanthropy gives the non-profit hospital some latitude for inefficiency, and this, among other things, tends to forestall entry by profit-making firms. An additional problem exists if the hospital is simply reimbursed by a third party for its costs. By removing the budget constraint, incentives for least-cost production are weakened."

C. Theoretical

1.49 Newhouse, Joseph P., and Phelps, Charles E. "Price and Income Elasticities for Medical Care Services." In THE ECONOMICS OF HEALTH AND MEDICAL CARE, Proceedings of a conference held by the International Economic Association, April 1973, Tokyo, edited by Mark Perlman, pp. 139-62. New York: John Wiley and Sons, 1973.

A. C^S

B. "This paper develops a framework for estimating demand for medical care, expanding Grossman's 'investment model' in three significant ways: multiple medical inputs are allowed in [the] production of health, reimbursement insurance is introduced (altering the net price of care) and choice of different 'styles' of care is allowed. Demand curves are estimated from 1963 United States household survey data, with the analysis limited to those with positive observed quantities of service. Use of explicit parameters from insurance policies to defined net price is a unique empirical aspect of this paper. Price elasticities of demand for hospital, physician office and hospital out-patient services are found to be small, all lying below 0.2 in absolute value. Wage income elasticities are positive and non-wage income is found to have no effect on demand, both as hypothesized by the model. Insurance coverage is also shown to influence price of services used, as does wage income and the quantity of services demanded."

C. Theoretical, quantitative methods

See also: *ibid*

(1) "Summary Record of Discussion." ECONOMICS OF HEALTH, pp. 194-96.

(2) Grossman, Michael. THE DEMAND FOR HEALTH: A THEORETICAL AND EMPIRICAL INVESTIGATION (entry G.28).

1.50 Pauly, Mark V. "Efficiency, Incentives and Reimbursement for Health Care." INQUIRY 7 (March 1970): 114-31.

A. C^S, P^S, FK

B. Attention is here given to "the several sources of ineffi-ciency that can arise in the provision of health care, the or-ganizations or persons who provide or consume that care, and the incentive schemes implied by various ways--actually used or potentially usable--of paying for health care." Specifically, Dr. Pauly attempts to "show how incentives affect the three major components in the medical system--the hospital, the physician, and the consumer--with respect to [the] various sources of efficiency [or inefficiency]." Also discussed are the effects of reimbursement incentives on: (1) the total out-put of physician services; (2) the locus of patient treatment, whether it be as an inpatient or in some other capacity; (3) the way in which physicians are paid; (4) the organization of the provision of physician care; (5) hospital production; and (6) the total quantity and mix of medical care the consumer uses.

1.51 _____. "Hospital Capital Investment: The Roles of Demand, Profits, and Physicians." JOURNAL OF HUMAN RESOURCES 9 (Winter 1974): 7-20.

A. PK

B. "After considering existing studies of hospital capital investment...some preliminary tests of a model of capital investment by short-term general hospitals" are provided. Pauly and Redisch originally developed this model (see entry 1.53) which emphasizes the role of the physician staff in explaining hospital behavior. It is a model which is "based on the assumption that hospitals are run to maximize the incomes of staff physicians. Optimal capital stock is shown to be related to physician income and hospital output. Analysis of a state-aggregate cross-section indicates that investment is a lagged response to output and physician income changes, while profits are not consistently an important determinant."

C. Theoretical, empirical, quantitative methods

1.52 Pauly, Mark V., and Drake, David F. "Effect of Third-Party Methods of Reimbursement on Hospital Performance." In EMPIRICAL STUDIES IN HEALTH ECONOMICS, edited by Herbert Klarman, pp. 297-314. Baltimore: Johns Hopkins Press, 1970.

A. P^S, FK

B. The study is based on an examination of four different reimbursement mechanisms which have been employed by Blue Cross plans in Illinois, Indiana, Michigan, and Wisconsin. Two integrated purposes are stipulated: (1) to discover whether differences in the methods of (third-party) payment for hospital services would affect the economic behavior of hospitals; and (2) to explain the basis for any performance differences that were found. Thus, the effectiveness of various reimbursement schemes is tested. "If different reimbursement schemes affect hospital performance in different ways, then the manner in which it is affected provides some information about how hospitals behave." [See "Comment" by Herbert E. Klarman, EMPIRICAL STUDIES, pp. 315-19.]

C. Empirical

1.53 Pauly, Mark [V.], and Redisch, Michael. "The Not-For-Profit Hospital as a Physicians' Cooperative." AMERICAN ECONOMIC REVIEW 63 (March 1973): 87-99.

A. $P^S L$, F

B. In the United States, hospital patients are subject to two separate billings--hospital charges for the use of capital and nonphysician labor, plus physician service charges. "This dual billing system has lead to a conceptually false dichotomy in much of the health economics literature. The physician and hospital are often viewed as independent economic entities selling services in functionally segmented health markets. This view appears to provide the rationale for the hospital administration-oriented, output maximization theories of hospital behavior." Pauly and Redisch basically reject this dichotomy and "propose an alternative model in which the physician emerges as a traditional income-maximizing economic agent who is 'discovered' in a decision-making role within this not-for-profit enterprise." The model is based on the assumption of net income maximization: "Specifically, we assume that the group of attending physicians on the hospital's staff enjoys de facto control of the hospital at any point in time. Given this assumption, we develop a model in which the hospital operates in such a way as to maximize the net income per member of the physician staff." The model is applied in three staffing contexts--closed staff, open staff, and a policy in which new physicians can be hired by the hospital.

1.54 Rafferty, John [A.]. "Measurement of Hospital Case-Mix: A Note on Alternative Patient Classifications." APPLIED ECONOMICS 4 (December 1972): 301-5.

A. P^S

B. Commonly used methods of measuring hospital output are here questioned, and specific attention is given to the questionable assumption of homogeniety--where this is implied when output is measured in the traditional units (number of patients or patient days of care). It is suggested, alternatively, that attention be given to the measurement and analysis of case-mix behavior since these variations in the patient census reflect variations in the output mix. The problem of specifying case types is addressed and several alternative methods of specification are examined through the use of index numbers in order to identify differences in sensitivity to case-mix variations. Methods for specifying case type are: (1) fifty leading diagnostic categories; (2) grouping the specific diagnostic codes into forty-four all-inclusive three-digit composite categories; (3) classification of patients under clinical service departments; (4) age; broad medical vs surgical designations. Methods (1) and (2) were found superior for identifying short-run variations which occur in hospital case-mix.

C. Quantitative methods

1.55 _____. "Patterns of Hospital Use: An Analysis of Short-Run Variations." JOURNAL OF POLITICAL ECONOMY 79 (January/February 1971): 154-65.

A. $P^S F$

B. "The purpose of this study is to identify and explain short-

run variations in the case-mix of a hospital's patient census."
Case-mix changes over time were studied at one hospital in
Anderson, Indiana, for the 1963-66 period. The thirty-five
most frequent causes of hospital admissions, accounting for approximately 35 percent of all nonobstetrical admissions, were
included in this study of 17,500 patients. Regarding variations
in the pattern of hospital use, it was found that "admissions in
seven categories increased and in six categories decreased in
months in which the rate of occupancy rose above normal levels. Illnesses in the latter group contrasted with those of the
former in a manner consistent with the hypothesis: they were
types for which hospital admission might reasonably be considered postponable or discretionary. Moreover, patient stays
for each group were, respectively, above and below the overall hospital average, indicating that a rationing of admissions
at high rates of occupancy not only altered case-mix but further intensified utilization by inducing an increase in the overall average patient stay." Further, it should be noted that:
"Since case-mix patterns [were] here found to be related to
occupancy, a part of the change in costs that accompanies
a change in output may be attributable to the altered package
of services produced at different utilization levels. Hence,
more should be known about the behavior of case-mix if we
are to be confident in our analysis of costs. Conclusions
based on cost comparisons between hospitals or drawn from
cross-sectional hospital cost data could be misleading if differences in mix are not considered along with differences in
capacity and utilization."

See also:

Rafferty, John. "A Comment on Incentive Reimbursement."
MEDICAL CARE 9 (November/December 1971): 518-20.

1.56 Reder, M.W. "Some Problems in the Economics of Hospitals." AMERI-
CAN ECONOMIC REVIEW: PAPERS AND PROCEEDINGS 55 (May 1965):
472-80.

A. $P^S PK$

B. Some behavioral and policy implications that derive from non-
profit hospitals are examined. In particular, attention is focused
on some of the obstacles to efficient hospital use which are
associated with the nonprofit status. "Obstacles" included in
the discussion are: (1) determining the socially optimal stock
of hospital facilities; (2) achieving the optimum use of these
facilities, given the possibilities of substitution among inputs
and outputs; (3) both the random and price elasticity qualities
of demand; (4) cost differentials; (5) facilities duplication.

1.57 Redisch, Michael. "Hospital Inflationary Mechanisms." Paper read at
Western Economics Association meetings, 10-12 June 1974, Las Vegas,

Published where ?

Nevada.

A. P^{S}F

B. "This paper documents how hospital costs have increased in the post-Medicare period.....[The] main thrust of this paper [is] to measure actual changes in 'intensity' of service and to relate these changes to changes in costs....A way to provide consistent hospital output measures over time is proposed, and a hedonic cost index for hospital care is constructed and estimated" in an effort to answer the following specific research question: "What part of the increase in cost per PDA [Patient Days Adjusted] and cost per ADMA [Admissions Adjusted] in a sample of over 200 short-term general hospitals can be related to the increased intensity of care as measured by a changing vector of medical services normalized on PDA's and on ADMA's? More than one-third of the increase in hospital costs [for 1968-1971] is found to be related to more intensive use of a small set of ancillary services."

C. Empirical, quantitative methods

1.58 Ro, Kong-Kyun. "Incremental Pricing Would Increase Efficiency in Hospitals." INQUIRY 6 (March 1969): 3-18.

A. P^{S}L, F

B. Incremental (marginal) pricing--applied both to hospital charges and the pay scale of hospital personnel--is suggested as a means of promoting social as well as private efficiency in the hospital industry. An increase in efficiency would derive from better utilization of facilities and better satisfaction of consumer and worker preferences. Current pricing patterns serve to foster admissions imbalances (weekly peaks/troughs) and therefore utilization imbalances--admissions generally peak at the beginning of any given week leaving relatively low census and therefore relatively low utilization (of services, manpower, physical capital) near the end of a week.

C. Empirical

1.59 _____. "Interactions among Variables Affecting Hospital Utilization." HEALTH SERVICES RESEARCH 8 (Winter 1973): 298-308.

A. C^S

B. "For purposes of developing a more refined basis for prediction of hospital utilization using readily available demographic variables, data for some 9,000 patients admitted to twenty-two short-term general hospitals in the Pittsburgh area are analyzed to determine the relationship of age, sex, and race to hospital use. Significant differences in length of stay and number of services used are found for various combinations of these variables when a form of multiple regression is used that allows for interaction effects among the variables." The article demonstrates an alternative dummy variable approach using the least-squares regression method. ("The method consists of arranging all possible combinations of dummy variables in a special way and forcing the intercept to zero.")

C. Empirical, quantitative methods

1.60 _____. "Patient Characteristics, Hospital Characteristics, and Hospital Use." In ESSAYS IN THE ECONOMICS OF HEALTH AND MEDICAL CARE, edited by V.R. Fuchs, pp. 69-96. New York: National Bureau of Economic Research, 1972.

A. C^S, P^S

B. In the introduction to his article, Ro notes that recent empirical studies have revealed two sets of systematic relationships--"one between the patterns of hospital use and the socioeconomic characteristics of patients and the other between hospital use and hospital characteristics." He further states that "two distinct theories of the economics of consumption of hospital services have emerged" in this context. The model developed by Ro is an attempt to integrate these two theories. One theory postulates that hospital use is determined through the interaction between patients and doctors. Choice-conditioning consumption factors resemble the usual list in the economics of consumption and include medical conditions, personal and situational factors. The other theory assumes that the economics of consumption has no role in explaining hospital use. "Production of hospital services is envisioned as largely determined by technological imperatives and productive facilities available as well as institutional characteristics of individual hospitals." In Ro's integrative model: "Consumption of hospital services is hypothesized as a composite effect of the joint interaction among physicians, patients, and hospitals. The direct interaction is envisioned as taking place between physicians and patients. Hospital characteristics come into the picture as a factor influencing this interaction." The model is tested by using twenty-two Pittsburgh area hospitals and 9,000 patients admitted in 1963.

C. Empirical, quantitative methods

1.61 Rosenthal, Gerald D. THE DEMAND FOR GENERAL HOSPITAL FACILITIES. Hospital Monograph Series no. 14. Chicago: American Hospital Association, 1964. 101 p.

A. C^S, P^SPK

B. This monograph is divided into three parts. Part 1 "presents the dimensions of the hospital 'system' and examines previous attempts to estimate the requirements for general hospital facilities. The development of the concept of 'adequacy' is related to the actual practice of using demand." In part 2 (chapters 3-6), a new method of estimating the demand for general hospital facilities is set forth. It encompasses theoretical considerations in developing a facilities-demand model, development of such a model, factors associated with demand and the nature of this association, model estimation regarding the demand for patient days of care, and the problem of estimating the facilities needed to meet a given demand for patient days of care. The concluding section, part 3, "uses the estimates developed in part 2 to evaluate current methods of estimating bed requirements and to explore possible applicability of the new technique to predicting future requirements." Included in part 3 are the influence of facilities supply on demand levels, implications of Rosenthal's model for the Hill-Burton standards, and the effect of need (not demand) assumptions on estimates of facilities required.

C. Empirical, quantitative methods

1.62 _____. "Price Elasticity of Demand for Short-Term General Hospital Services." In EMPIRICAL STUDIES IN HEALTH ECONOMICS, edited by Herbert Klarman, pp. 101-17. Baltimore: Johns Hopkins Press, 1970.

A. C^S

B. "The object of the analysis presented here is to examine the degree to which the length of stay is associated with various price-payment factors for groups of patients with considerably more homogeneous characteristics than a broad-scale analysis will allow." Two specific price-payment measures are analyzed--cash outlay as a percentage of the total bill, and average daily room charge--as determinants of length of stay. A corollary implicit analysis is also developed, relating to the hypothesis that certain diagnostic categories will be more likely to show a high price elasticity of length of stay than others. [See "Comment" by Victor R. Fuchs, EMPIRICAL STUDIES, pp. 118-20.]

C. Empirical, quantitative methods

1.63 Ruchlin, H.S.; Pointer, D.D.; and Cannedy, L.L. "A Comparison of For-Profit Investor-Owned Chain and Nonprofit Hospitals." INQUIRY 10 (December 1973): 13-23.

A. $P^S PK, F$

B. A brief review of some major issues regarding the relative merits and demerits of nonprofit and for-profit control introduces this study. Selectivity and social comment, types of care, and financial considerations represent the areas of concern. Next, their methodology in developing a matched sample of fifty-six hospital pairs, each pair having one investor-owned chain and one nonprofit voluntary or state/local government hospital, is described. Their empirical findings tentatively suggest some financial "skimming" and "cream skimming" (e.g., admission of lower-risk patients), but the authors also emphasize the need for further research.

C. Empirical

See also:

(1) Rafferty, John, and Schweitzer, Stuart O. "Comparison of For-Profit and Nonprofit Hospitals: A Re-evaluation." INQUIRY 11 (December 1974): 304-9.

Not in author/title list

The authors argue that the research design of Ruchlin, et al., leads to underestimation of the degree of skimming practiced by for-profit hospitals. They identify this bias and try to estimate its degree through an empirical analysis.

(2) Ruchlin, H.S.; Pointer, D.D.; and Cannedy, L.L. "Reply." INQUIRY 4 (December 1974): 310-11.

1.64 Russell, Louise B. "The Impact of the Extended-Care Facility Benefit on Hospital Use and Reimbursements Under Medicare." JOURNAL OF HUMAN RESOURCES 8 (Winter 1973): 57-72.

A. P^{S}F

B. "The coverage of extended-care facilities (ECFs) under Medicare was intended as a means of shortening patient stays in short-term hospitals and reducing the overall costs of the program....In this study, regression analysis is applied to Medicare data on average hospital stay by state to determine whether higher levels of ECF use are associated with shorter hospital stays. The regression analysis is then extended to permit examination of the impact of ECF use on Part A (hospital insurance) reimbursements. Two basic conclusions emerge:

1. ECF use, measured by ECF admissions per 100 short-stay hospital admissions, is significantly associated with shorter hospital stays. Estimates based on the regressions indicate that stays for Medicare patients in short-stay hospitals in the U.S. were about 1.4 days shorter in 1967 and 1.8 days shorter in 1968 because of ECF use.

2. The shortened hospital stays have contributed to reduced outlays under Part A of the program. Estimated savings in hospital reimbursements were substantially greater than outlays for ECF use in both 1967 and 1968."

C. Empirical, quantitative methods

1.65 Salkever, David. "A Microeconometric Study of Hospital Cost Inflation."

JOURNAL OF POLITICAL ECONOMY 80 (November/December 1972): 1144-66.

A. P^S

B. "The formulation of effective inflation control policy requires the identification of the causes of cost inflation and information about the quantitative importance of various causes." A behavioral model is developed "(1) to explain why the rate of cost inflation varies across hospitals and over time and (2) to determine the most important causes of cost inflation." The study's empirical base is "average cost per day for a group of private nonprofit short-term hospitals in southeastern New York State from 1961-67. Average cost per day is assumed to be a multiplicative function of factors affecting the demand for hospital services, measures of factor costs, hospital preferences, and last year's level of average cost per day. The empirical results indicate that a variety of factors contributed to cost inflation in these hospitals but that average cost per day responds slowly to changes in these factors." Salkever concludes his paper with the following comment: "The development of and experimentation with new reimbursement methods offers a promising area for development of cost control policy and for an application of a micro model. But the potential for micro studies in this area will not be realized unless the designers of such experiments make provision for the necessary data at the local level."

C. Empirical, quantitative methods

1.66 Schneider, J.B. "Measuring, Evaluating and Redesigning Hospital-Physician-Patient Spatial Relationship in Metropolitan Areas." INQUIRY 5 (June 1968): 24-43.

A. PK

B. The spatial or locational aspect of organizing medical practice is here emphasized. Specifically, the spatial distribution of physicians' offices and residences is examined in the context of patient residential patterns and the locational pattern of the urban general short-term hospital system. (Empirical application is to the Cincinnati metropolitan area.) This spatial analysis is concerned with two types of phenomena: the size-location patterns of the physical facilities, and the movement patterns set up by the human components as they interact with each other during a treatment cycle. To develop health facility systems which display a high degree of geographic balance requires, in part, the development of methods of analysis that describe and measure the spatial complexities involved in a consistent and standardized manner. This methodological aid to decision-making constitutes the essence of Dr. Schneider's study.

C. Empirical, methodological

1.67 Stevens, Carl M. "Hospital Market Efficiency: The Anatomy of the Supply Response." In EMPIRICAL STUDIES IN HEALTH ECONOMICS, edited by Herbert Klarman, pp. 229-48. Baltimore: Johns Hopkins Press, 1970.

A. P^S

B. The main concern is hospital market performance measured by an efficient or optimum rate of output (defined as an efficient supply response to demand events). Basic to the realization of this concern is Stevens's preparatory discussion of hospital market structure and conduct. A significant supply response element (link) was found to be accommodation (though not merely passive) to the demands of staff physicians. [See "Comment" by Edwin S. Mills, EMPIRICAL STUDIES, pp. 249-51.]

C. Theoretical

1.68 Vogel, Ronald J., and Morrall, John F. III. "The Impact of Medicaid on State and Local Health and Hospitals Expenditures, with Special Reference to Blacks." JOURNAL OF HUMAN RESOURCES 8 (Spring 1973): 202-11.

For annotation see 4.9.

1.69 Worthington, Paul N. "Capital-Labor Ratios in Short-Term Voluntary Hospitals." INQUIRY 11 (June 1974): 98-111.

A. HK, PK

B. "In this paper, an effort is made to commence the task of filling [the] gap in empirical knowledge [regarding uniformities in the use of capital]. Measurement of capital stock for a sample of 38 short-term voluntary hospitals, all in New York City, are employed to examine the use of capital. The purpose is to provide an empirical estimate of the extent to which capital is substituted for labor....The results of the inquiry show highly responsive capital-labor ratios to variations in hospital wage. This elasticity, interpreted as an empirical measure of the ease of substitution, is estimated to be 2 in non-teaching hospitals and near unity in teaching hospitals." The condition of and the relative extent or ease of capital-labor substitution suggest "first of all, that planning or regulating mechanisms can probably be more effective in promoting economic efficiency by concentrating on the mix or assortment of services produced by a facility rather than on plans and designs that outline the way capital is to be used. Second, the findings indicate that the demand for capital may be highly sensitive to allocative effects. Third, the comparatively high elasticity of substitution implies a rising trend in capital costs as a proportion of total hospital costs."

C. Theoretical, empirical, quantitative methods

1.70 Yett, Donald E., and Sloan, Frank A. "Migration Patterns of Recent Medical School Graduates." INQUIRY 11 (June 1974): 125-42.

For annotation see 2.25.

Chapter 3

PHYSICIAN OFFICE PRACTICE

2.1 Bailey, Richard M. "Economies of Scale in Medical Practice." In EM-
PIRICAL STUDIES IN HEALTH ECONOMICS, edited by Herbert Klarman,
pp. 255-73. Baltimore: Johns Hopkins Press, 1970.

A. P^SL

B. In the context of medical group practice, this paper reviews
some current thought on medical practice and medical services
production; attempts to clarify some of the implicit theories
and assumptions that are basic to current thought; and offers
a new interpretation of the production process based on Bailey's
recent research findings. The basic question here is not
whether economies of scale exist "but where they are to
be found and how significant they are....[The] most important public policy issue is how we can increase physician productivity, not how we can achieve internal economies of scale
in the practice of medicine." [See "Comment" by Melvin W.
Reder, EMPIRICAL STUDIES, pp. 274-77.]

C. Empirical

2.2 _____. "Philosophy, Faith, Fact and Fiction in the Production of Medical Services." INQUIRY 7 (March 1970): 37-53.

A. P^SL

B. Dr. Bailey introduces his paper by identifying what he
believes to be the major problem in research in health
economics: "Too many economists want to fit the world
of medicine and health care to the economic models that
they cherish; too few want to view the medical world as
it really is and then attempt to analyze it, using the economic tools appropriate to the task." This piecemeal analysis
could well result in the development of "disastrous public policy." It is therefore necessary to properly integrate, within
medical economics, elementary concepts, institutional knowledge, and social judgment--an integration attempted by
Bailey in the context of medical services produced by phy-

sicians in their outpatient setting. The matter of linking "medical service inputs to the socially desirable output of improved health" is a most difficult problem, and an understanding of medical service inputs (in which the physician is the determining factor) is crucial in establishing linkages. Physician inputs are treated in the context of physician productivity and economies of scale.

2.3   Benham, L[ee].; Maurizi, A.; and Reder, M.[W.]. "Migration, Location and Remuneration of Medical Personnel: |Physicians and Dentists." REVIEW OF ECONOMICS AND STATISTICS 50 (August 1968): 332-47.

A. HK

B. "This study investigates how well the distribution of the national stocks of medics (...physicians and dentists) among areas corresponds to the distribution of population, and what influence is exerted by other variables such as effective demand for medical service, barriers to migration, and the location preferences of medics." The specific economic characteristics studied include population, per capita income, volume of training facilities, degree of urbanization, and average income of medical personnel. The analysis was carried on at the state level for ten-year intervals, 1930-60. Linear regression equations were estimated relating numbers of medical personnel to the above variables. These estimates indicated that the number of medical personnel in a state mainly depends upon its population and, to a lesser degree, upon its per capita income. After reporting their regression results, the authors present "an exploratory attempt to estimate the parameters of a simple structural model that determines the location of medics."

C. Empirical, quantitative methods

2.4   Evans, Robert G. "Supplier-Induced Demand: Some Empirical Evidence and Implications." In THE ECONOMICS OF HEALTH AND MEDICAL CARE, Proceedings of a conference held by the International Economic Association, April 1973, Tokyo, edited by Mark Perlman, pp. 162-73. New York: John Wiley and Sons, 1973.

A. C^S, $P^S L$, F

B. "The professional relationship arises from the significant information differential between physician and patient, and permits the physician to exert direct, non-price influence on the demand for his own services. If the economic status of the physician affects the level and direction of such influence exerted, then models of the demand for care which do not include explicit consideration of supplier behavior are incompletely specified. This paper outlines the effect on demand analyses of two alternative specifications of physician behavior, and notes that each can lead to 'perverse' response of price to increase in supply, or of quantity demanded to price. It then examines several pieces of empirical evidence from Canada and the United States which are consistent with substantial demand influence by physicians, with responses of generated output to physician stock around 80 percent through increases in supply of physician-initiated services. The conclusion is that policy to limit price inflation, correct 'shortages' or restrain unnecessary utilization cannot be based on conventional supply and demand models."

See also:

"Summary Record of Discussion." ECONOMICS OF HEALTH, pp. 196-99.

2.5   Fein, Rashi. THE DOCTOR SHORTAGE; AN ECONOMIC DIAGNOSIS. Washington, D.C.: Brookings Institution, 1967. 199 p.

A. C^S, P^S

B. This study examines the future demand for physicians' services and the future supply of physicians. It assesses alternative ways of meeting the growth in demand, and considers increasing the number of physicians as but one of these. Chapter 1 distinguishes between health, medical, and physician services on the one hand and manpower on the other. "...[It] is services, not manpower, that are demanded, supplied, and purchased." In chapter 2 ("Future Demand for Physicians' Services"), future services demand is examined in the context of the growth and changing structure of the population, the impact of Medicare, new discoveries in medicine, rising expectations, and possible changes in the proportion of in- and out-of-hospital care. Chapter 3 examines the supply of physicians-- including total supply, locational patterns, and the shift to specialization and some of its consequences. In chapter 4 (Productivity and Organization"), possible sources of increased productivity are analyzed, with emphasis first on group practice and then on the impact of paramedical personnel. The concluding chapter integrates demand and supply projections and suggests some policy implications.

C. Empirical, methodological

2.6   Feldstein, Martin S. "The Rising Price of Physicians' Services." REVIEW OF ECONOMICS AND STATISTICS 52 (May 1970): 121-33.

A. P^SF

B. "Traditional models of instantaneous or lagged adjustment cannot explain the substantial rise in the price of physicians' services during the period 1948 through 1966. An alternative aggregate econometric model is developed in which excess demand prevails throughout the sample period with no systematic tendency toward a clearing price. The primary qualitative results are: 1) the supply curve for physicians' services is downward sloping; 2) physicians increase prices when patients' ability to pay is improved by more complete insurance coverage--more than a third of the potential gain from improved insurance coverage was dissipated by these induced price increases; 3) greater use of paramedical personnel and supplies did not decrease the cost of physicians' services. A variety of other variables are also studied. Among the by-products of the analysis are revised estimates of the rates of increases of physicians' fees, output, and productivity." [Abstract from JOURNAL OF ECONOMIC LITERATURE]

C. Empirical, quantitative methods

See also:

(1) Brown, Douglas M., and Lapan, Harvey E. "The Rising Price of Physicians' Services: A Comment." REVIEW OF ECONOMICS AND STATISTICS 54 (February 1972): 101-5.

> The authors show that "(1) the positive price elasticity Feldstein obtains in trying to estimate the demand curve might result from difficulties in defining his price variable (and from the fact that insured and uninsured pay different prices), and (2) his supply estimates are biased because of his use of a dependent variable, inputs (paramedical personnel, equipment, etc.) as an independent variable in his supply equation."

(2) Feldstein, Martin S. "The Rising Price of Physicians' Services: A Reply." REVIEW OF ECONOMICS AND STATISTICS 54 (February 1972): 105-7.

2.7   Fuchs, Victor R., and Kramer, Marcia J. DETERMINANTS OF EXPENDITURES FOR PHYSICIANS' SERVICES IN THE UNITED STATES, 1948-68. National Bureau of Economic Research Occasional Paper 117. Washington, D.C.: Department of Health, Education and Welfare, Publication (HSM) 73-3013, December 1972. 63 p.

A. C^S, P^S

B. To accomplish their main objective--gaining a better understanding of the factors that determine expenditures for physicians' services in the United States--the authors analyze both trends over time and variations across states at a given point in time. Part 1 "provides a statistical decomposition of the growth of per capita expenditures at the national level. Major attention is focused on the sharp differences in the rate of change of this variable between the subperiods 1948-56 (4.1 per cent per annum) and 1956-66 (6.6 per cent per annum)." This differential is examined through consideration of price changes, insurance coverage, income, population, number and type of physicians, and medical technology. "The second part is concerned with the development and testing of a formal model to analyze the behavior of physicans and patients. Cross-sectional (state) data for 1966 are used to gain an understanding of variations in quantity of services per capita, physicians per capita, quantity of services per physician, and insurance coverage. The consequences for health of differences in the quantity of physicians' services are also explored." Their most significant finding was that "supply factors (technology and number of physicians) appear to be of decisive importance in determining the utilization of and expenditures for physicians' services."

C. Empirical, quantitative methods

2.8 Golladay, Frederick L.; Manser, Marilyn E.; and Smith, Kenneth R. "Scale Economies in the Delivery of Medical Care: A Mixed Integer Programming Analysis of Efficient Manpower Utilization." JOURNAL OF HUMAN RESOURCES 9 (Winter 1974): 50-62.

A. $P^S L$, F

B. "The purpose of this paper [was] to present a model of primary care which realistically represents both the technology of ambulatory care and the institutional constraints on the organization of resources. The paper...focused primarily on the notion that labor inputs must be purchased in discrete units-- which implies that both staffing patterns and optimal choices of technique are likely to depend on scale of practice. Empirical experiments with the model...demonstrated that both staffing and optimal techniques are indeed sensitive to scale of practice (measured by patient visits) and, furthermore, that suboptimal scale of practice results in substantially higher costs. The model also [revealed] that introduction of physician extenders into the medical care system increases the scale at which economies of staffing are obtained....[These exploratory and tentative] empirical results strongly support the view that the scale of practice is an important influence on efficient delegation. These conclusions imply that the needs for new health workers will clearly depend upon the modes of organization and the scales of practice prevailing in the future."

See also:

Smith, K.R.; Miller, M.; and Golladay, F.L. "An Analysis of the Optimal Use of Inputs in the Production of Medical Services." (entry 2.24)

2.9 Kehrer, Barbara H., and Intriligator, Michael D. "Task Delegation in Physician Office Practice." INQUIRY 11 (December 1974): 292-99.

A. $P^S L$

B. "The relation of task delegation in physicians' office practice to certain practice characteristics bearing on the degree of observed delegation is the special focus of this paper. Previous studies of task delegation are reviewed and task performance data obtained in a recent survey...[AMA, 1971] are

described. Subsequent sections utilize data obtained in the
AMA survey to investigate the frequency of delegation in various specialties, delegation frequency by type of practice, regional variation in delegation, and the types of allied health
personnel performing delegated tasks. It appears that the propensity for delegation is greater 1) with respect to easily rou-
tinized tasks, as compared with activities requiring clinical
judgment; 2) in group practices; 3) in the Western regions of
the United States; and 4) to registered nurses, rather than to
other types of allied health personnel. These findings demonstrate the possibility for a significant increase in the extent of
delegation of functions to allied health personnel in the office
practice context."

C. Empirical

2.10 Kessel, Reuben A. "Price Discrimination in Medicine." JOURNAL OF
LAW AND ECONOMICS 1 (October 1958): 20-53.

A. P^SL, F

B. "The primary objective of this paper, which is an essay in
positive economics, is to show by empirical evidence that the
standard textbook rationalization of what appears to be a con-
tradiction of the law of markets is correct. It [is] argued that
the discriminating monopoly model is valid for understanding
the pricing of medical services, and that each individual buyer
of medical services that are produced jointly with hospital care
constitutes a unique, separable market. In the process of presenting evidence supporting this thesis, other closely related
phenomena [are] considered. These are (1), why the AMA
favors medical insurance prepayment plans that provide money
to be used to buy medical services, but bitterly opposes comparable plans that provide instead of money, the service itself
and (2), why the AMA has opposed free medical care by the
Veterans Administration for veterans despite the enormous increase in the quantity of medical services demanded that would
result from the reduction to zero of the private costs of medical care for such a large group....The body of this paper
is divided into five sections. These are, in order of presenta-
tion, a hypothesis alternative to the price discrimination hypothesis, a history of the development of the powers that enable
organized medicine to organize effectively a discriminating
monopoly, evidence supporting the validity of the discriminating monopoly model for understanding the pricing of medical
services, and lastly an application of the discriminating monopoly model to rationalize many characteristics of the medical
profession that have been hitherto thought of as either anoma-
lies or behavior that could best be explained as non-economic
phenomena."

2.11 Klarman, Herbert E. "Approaches to Moderating the Increases in Medical

Care Costs." MEDICAL CARE 7 (May/June 1969): 175-90.

For annotation see 1.32.

2.12 _____. "Increase in the Cost of Physician and Hospital Services." IN-QUIRY 7 (March 1970): 22-36.

For annotation see 1.33.

2.13 Lindsay, Cotton M. "Real Returns to Medical Education." JOURNAL OF HUMAN RESOURCES 8 (Summer 1973): 331-48.

For annotation see G.40.

2.14 Masson, Robert T., and Wu, S. "Price Discrimination for Physicians' Services." JOURNAL OF HUMAN RESOURCES 9 (Winter 1974): 63-79.

A. $P^S F$

B. To analyze physician pricing behavior, the authors introduce "information cost explicitly, [thus generating the result that] even if the elasticity of market demand is less than one, and if all or most of the agents in the market are profit maximiz-ers,...price discrimination will be practiced by all sellers. We first develop a model showing that information costs insu-late physicians' markets from one another; and assuming that physicians maximize profits, such an industry would develop price discrimination by income. Next we incorporate the role of charity in the model and conclude that we need both a profit motive and a charity motive to adequately explain the evidence on physician pricing and demand elasticity. Finally, after a brief look at the policies of the AMA, we examine the history of physician pricing behavior and interpret it in the light of the conclusions from our model."

C. Theoretical, quantitative methods

2.15 Monsma, George N., Jr. "Marginal Revenue and the Demand for Phy-sicians' Services." In EMPIRICAL STUDIES IN HEALTH ECONOMICS, edited by Herbert Klarman, pp. 145-60. Baltimore: Johns Hopkins Press, 1970.

A. C^S, $P^S F$

B. "This study shows that conditions necessary for [the] assump-tion [that quantity demanded is independent of marginal reve-nue to the supplier] to be valid are not present in the case of the demand for physicians' services. It also suggests ways in which, given the prevailing institutional arrangements, the demand for physicians' services would be expected to vary in response to the marginal return to the physician and examines the available empirical evidence to see whether, in fact, the demand for physicians' services is influenced by the marginal revenue physicians receive in the manner suggested by the theory."

C. Theoretical, empirical

2.16 Newhouse, Joseph P. "The Economics of Group Practice." JOURNAL OF HUMAN RESOURCES 8 (Winter 1973): 37–56.

A. $P^S L$, F

B. "This article presents a theoretical and empirical discussion of how costs of outpatient medical practice vary with the size of the group providing services. It focuses upon an element which seems to have been ignored by those advocating increased emphasis on group practice, namely, the incentives facing the individual physician to keep the cost of his practice down and his work effort high. Cost and revenue-sharing schemes are more prevalent as group size increases; therefore, any individual physician is less likely to have to bear the financial consequences of his decisions. Likewise, the reward he obtains from additional work effort falls. Thus, we would predict that total costs would rise as an individual physician's share of costs falls because of greater x-inefficiency. We would also predict that hours of work would fall as the individual physician's share of marginal revenue falls. The situation reaches an extreme in hospital outpatient clinics....The evidence presented in the article tends to support these propositions."

C. Theoretical, empirical, quantitative methods

2.17 _____. "A Model of Physician Pricing." SOUTHERN ECONOMIC JOURNAL 37 (October 1970): 174–83.

A. P^S

B. This paper attempts to shed some light on the question of whether the market for physician services can be better characterized as monopolistic or competitive. "Knowledge of market characteristics is fundamental to sound public policy in the area. It is also important for the proper specification of an econometric model of the medical care sector." The related matters of consumer ignorance and low cross-elasticity of demand between any two physicians provide an introductory base for the development and subsequent testing of two alternative models regarding the market for physician services—model I is that of a monopoly, and model II is a competitive one. General practitioner (office visit) price and income data, plus the number of such practitioners, are used to test the models. Newhouse concludes: "Although our tests are relatively weak because of the small number of observations, they all accord with a priori expectations in indicating that the market for physicians' services is monopolistic rather than competitive....Consumer ignorance about price and quality...leads to low cross-elasticities of demand....If this explanation is correct, the system is inherently monopolistic, since competitive force of the marketplace cannot readily drive price to average cost."

C. Empirical, quantitative methods

See also:

(1) Frech, H.E. III, and Ginsburg, Paul B. "Physician Pricing: Monopolistic or Competitive: Comment." SOUTHERN ECONOMIC JOURNAL 38 (April 1972): 573-77.

> The authors attempt to demonstrate that inconsistencies in the Newhouse analysis "make it impossible for any of his statistical tests to distinguish between monopolistic and competitive physician pricing policy."

(2) Newhouse, Joseph P., and Sloan, Frank A. "Physician Pricing: Monopolistic or Competitive: Reply." SOUTHERN ECONOMIC JOURNAL 38 (April 1972): 577-80.

> Acknowledging some error, as pointed out in the Frech and Ginsburg "Comment," the authors continue to assert that "the general thrust of the evidence is clear. [There is]...the existence of substantial discretionary power on the part of the physician and hence to a non-competitive market."

2.18 Newhouse, Joseph P., and Phelps, Charles E. "Price and Income Elasticities for Medical Care Services." In THE ECONOMICS OF HEALTH AND MEDICAL CARE, Proceedings of a conference held by the International Economic Association, April 1973, Tokyo, edited by Mark Perlman, pp. 139-62. New York: John Wiley and Sons, 1973.

For annotation see 1.49.

2.19 Pauly, Mark V. "Efficiency, Incentives and Reimbursement for Health Care." INQUIRY 7 (March 1970): 114-31.

For annotation see 1.50.

2.20 Reinhardt, U. "A Product Function for Physician Services." REVIEW OF ECONOMICS AND STATISTICS 54 (February 1972): 55-66.

A. P^SL

B. Reinhardt attempts to contribute to an understanding of the technical and economic determinants of physician productivity. "Using a simple model of physician behavior and a nationwide cross-section sample of physicians, the study seeks to identify the effects of auxiliary personnel and of the mode of practice (solo or group) on the physician's rate of output." A stratified sample of 2,000 physicians for the years 1965 and 1967 was used as input to the estimation, via ordinary least squares, of physician production functions. Variables included in the estimation process were: (1) data on income and expenses; (2) the physician's weekly rate of office, hospital, and home visits; (3) number of hours per week spent by the physician on various professional activities; (4) number of aides employed by the physician (including their salaries); (5) the physician's medical specialty; and (6) type of organization (solo or group). After empirical results are presented, the matter of optimum level of paramedical-aide employment is discussed. It is concluded "that the average American physician could profitably employ roughly twice the number of aides he currently employs and thus increase his hourly rate of output by about 25 per cent above its current level. This figure takes on added meaning when it is recalled that a mere increase of 4 per cent in average physician productivity in the United States would add more to the aggregate supply of physician services than would the entire current graduating class from American medical schools."

C. Empirical, quantitative methods

2.21 Rimlinger, Gaston V., and Steele, Henry B. "An Economic Interpretation of the Spatial Distribution of Physicians in the U.S." SOUTHERN ECONOMIC JOURNAL 30 (July 1963): 1-12

A. HK

B. This article begins with a description of the empirical relationship between the ratios of physicians to both population and regional per capita incomes. This ratio rises with increases in per capita income. Given this finding, several hypotheses are then developed to examine the economic variables that may account for the observed relationship. "The determinants of physician distribution, given the regional distribution of income, were found to be (1) the relation of fees to patient income, (2) the relation of demand for physician services to patient income, and (3) the behavior of physicians with respect to price competition, income maximization, desire for leisure, and geographic mobility." Using this theoretical base, an empirical analysis of these three distributional determinants is next set forth. The data includes limited information on physician incomes, physician visits, and medical expenditures. Economic implications of the findings are also provided.

2.22 Ruffin, Roy J., and Leigh, Duane E. "Charity, Competition, and the Pricing of Doctors' Services." JOURNAL OF HUMAN RESOURCES 8 (Spring 1973): 212-22.

A. $P^S F$

B. "There are two basic explanations of price discrimination in medicine....[One is] the theory of a price-discriminating monopolist...[and the other is] price discrimination by the operation of a charity. This paper develops a charity-competition model in which price discrimination emerges as a consequence of utility maximization by the individual doctor and the necessity of market equilibrium." The authors develop their model in relation to a paper by R.A. Kessel ("Price Discrimination in Medicine," entry 1.31). "Section 1 shows that Kessel's 'crucial experiment,' which purports to eliminate the charity model, is faulty; it also reviews Kessel's argument that the AMA has the power to discipline individual doctors and indicates that he failed to offer any evidence on the main point. Section 2 spells out a formal economic model combining both charity and competition. Section 3 carries out certain simple tests of the monopoly and charity-competition models, showing that the latter is superior on all counts....Also, it is shown that the model can be used as a foundation for modifying the basic a priori specification in Martin Feldstein's econometric model of the market for doctors' services and that the modification should change the estimates significantly." (Feldstein's paper, "The Rising Price of Physicians' Services," is entry 2.6).

C. Theoretical, quantitative methods

2.23 Schneider, J.B. "Measuring, Evaluating and Redesigning Hospital-Physician-Patient Spatial Relationships in Metropolitan Areas." INQUIRY 5 (June 1968): 24-43.

For annotation see 1.66.

2.24 Smith, Kenneth R.; Miller, Marianne; and Golladay, Fredrick L. "An Analysis of the Optimal Use of Inputs in the Production of Medical Services." JOURNAL OF HUMAN RESOURCES 7 (Spring 1972): 208-25.

A. $P^S L$, F

B. "The purpose of this paper is to explore the implications of employing physicians' assistants in delivering primary care. It seeks to identify the optimal role of paramedical personnel and to assess the impact of efficient delegation of tasks on the productivity of the physician, his opportunities for leisure, and the cost of care. The study proceeds by first identifying the technical opportunities for delegation and the specific demands for medical services imposed on the primary care practice. It then analyzes these data in an activity analysis model of the practice in order to identify efficient patterns of delegation and to assess the implications of delegation. The study responds to the following specific questions: To what extent can the supply of medical services delivered by an individual practitioner be expanded through efficient delegation of tasks? What are the derived demands for specific types of paraprofessionals if the practice is efficiently organized? What is the optimal pattern of staffing for practices of different sizes? What is the impact of delegation on the opportunities for leisure for the physician? What is the cost of additional leisure to the physician if obtained through delegation? How are the potential gains in physician productivity affected by legal, professional, or sociological restrictions on the delegation of tasks? What is the impact of efficient delegation on the net income from practice?"

C. Empirical, quantitative methods

2.25 Yett, Donald E., and Sloan, Frank A. "Migration Patterns of Recent Medical School Graduates." INQUIRY 11 (June 1974): 125-42.

A. HK

B. Using 1966 data, the authors develop a model which "seeks to explain the locational choices of recent medical school graduates, rather than the spatial distribution of all physicians. One expects them [new entrants] to be most responsive to policy inducements..." Six categories of explanatory variables are considered in model development: "1) previous attachment to the state, 2) income, 3) barriers to entry, 4) opportunities for professional development, 5) general environmental conditions, and 6) effort required to secure a given income level (alternatively, time available for leisure pursuits)." Yett and Sloan demonstrate "that recently-trained physicians have a higher propensity to establish practices in states where their previous level of attachment (i.e., the 'events' birth, medical school, internship, and residency) is strongest and most recent ...[and]...that certain measures related to income growth and general environmental conditions exert a significant influence on the location decisions of this group." Some policy implications of these findings conclude the paper, with special emphasis on the matter of state attachment deriving from the "events" previously noted.

C. Empirical, quantitative methods

2.26 Zeckhauser, Richard, and Eliastam, Michael. "The Productivity Potential of the Physician Assistant." JOURNAL OF HUMAN RESOURCES 9 (Winter 1974): 95-116.

A. P^SL

B. "This paper develops a production function methodology to estimate the potential contribution of physician assistants in the delivery of medical care. This methodology is applied to a paradigm delivery mode, an urban health center. Following upon a discussion of the possibilities for delegation and the efficient assignment of medical tasks to physician assistants, a numerical production function is estimated for physicians and physician assistants working together. When taking on his most productive assignments, it is found, a physician assistant can replace half of a full-time physician." [The analysis here is directed to Type A assistants--those delegated by the National Academy of Science as having highly developed skills and assuming general responsibilities. The methodology could, it is asserted, also be applied to Types B, C and D.]

C. Methodological

Chapter 4

HEALTH INSURANCE

3.1   Baird, Charles W. "A Proposal for Financing the Purchase of Health Services." JOURNAL OF HUMAN RESOURCES 5 (Winter 1970): 89-105.

A. C^S

B. "The porposal is made to grant tax credits against the personal income tax for 75 to 80 percent of all health care expenditures other than those made for the initial visit to a physician per illness. This in effect provides all individuals in the United States with a health insurance policy which has deductible and coinsurance clauses to cope with the problem of moral hazard and the generally uninsurable routine health expenditures. The premium paid by each individual--the amount that his tax bill must increase to offset the decrease in tax revenues from the credits--would depend on his income. Both a progressive and a proportional premium scheme are investigated. The advantages of such a scheme are that it would obviate the necessity for growing government involvement in the health market and that it, more clearly than existing government programs, would benefit the poor sick more than the wealthy sick."

C. Theoretical

See also:

(1) Weiss, Jeffrey H. "A Proposal for Financing the Purchase of Health Services: A Comment." JOURNAL OF HUMAN RESOURCES 6 (Winter 1971): 123-24.

Not in AfT

(2) Baird, Charles W. "A Market Solution to Medical Inflation: A Reply." JOURNAL OF HUMAN RESOURCES 6 (Winter 1971): 125-29.

3.2   Cooper, Michael. "Economics of Need: The Experience of the British Health Service." In THE ECONOMICS OF HEALTH AND MEDICAL CARE, Proceedings of a conference held by the International Economic Association, April 1973, Tokyo, edited by Mark Perlman, pp. 89-107. New York: John Wiley and Sons, 1973.

For annotation see 6.1.

3.3   Eilers, Robert D. "The Changing Environment for Blue Shield." MEDI-
       CAL CARE 6 (January/February 1968): 55-68.

       A. P^S

       B. Facets involved in the provision of physicians' benefits, the
       lifeblood of Blue Shield, are here considered. Present condi-
       tions and likely developments are discussed "primarily in con-
       nection with private health care coverages, although mention
       [is] made of governmental efforts, which suggest a need for
       change on the part of Blue Shield plans if they are to retain
       their vibrancy and possibly to expand their influence." Spe-
       cific attention is given to: (1) the incentives of organizational
       growth and profit in a competitive market, (2) an expansion
       of the population covered, (3) the health care package--in-
       cluding catastrophic coverage, coverage for mental illness and
       nervous conditions, home-care coverage, benefit adequacy,
       and the liberalization of benefits, (4) internal Blue Shield-
       Blue Cross disputes, (5) relationship with other insurance plans,
       (6) cost control (especially utilization review), (7) group prac-
       tice prepayment, (8) reimbursement arrangements, (9) rate-
       making practices, (10) Blue Shield image as viewed by physi-
       cians and consumers, (11) the regulatory environment, and
       (12) the influence of the federal government's increasing in-
       volvement. Blue Shield performance (actual and suggested)
       is examined in the context of each of these areas, and pri-
       marily in relation to other insurance companies.

3.4   _____. "Post-payment Medical Expense Coverage: A Proposed Salvation
       for Insured and Insurer." MEDICAL CARE 7 (May/June 1969): 191-208.

       A. FK

       B. "Post-payment is proposed as a supplement to current medi-
       cal expense coverages. Under post-payment, a Blue Cross-
       Blue Shield plan or insurance company would pay all of a
       policy-holder's medical expenses, possibly excluding certain
       minor items. The individual would repay the insurer for the
       difference between total medical expenses and his payment
       benefits, such repayment being over several months or years
       if desired. The interest on 'post-payment loans' would be
       lower than rates charged by commercial lending institutions.
       Bad-debt losses arising from post-payment could be offset by
       a low premium charge, discounting of bills, or through the
       interest charge. The post-payment recommendation presumes
       that purchasers of medical expense insurance will continue
       to be unwilling to pay the price for adequate prepayment
       coverage. Details concerning eligibility, benefits and pre-
       miums for post-payment are set forth. The implications of the
       new concept for insureds, insurers, hospitals, physicians and
       governmental programs are explored."

3.5 Fein, Rashi. "Impact of National Health Insurance Plans on Financing."
In NATIONAL HEALTH INSURANCE, Proceedings of the conference on
National Health Insurance held November 1970, University of Pennsylvania,
edited by Robert D. Eilers and Sue S. Moyerman, pp. 75-102. Homewood, Ill.: Richard D. Irwin, 1971.

A. FK

B. Dr. Fein begins with a discussion of "some of the reasons
that national health insurance has projected itself into the
limelight, [that] we may better understand some of the objectives of the program and some of the problems which it is
hoped NHI would solve." In a summary manner, Fein here
stresses "the need for general criteria concerning the implications of alternative methods of financing the government revenues." The second major section relates to problems in estimating
financing and distributional impact. Two major difficulties are
suggested: "The first difficulty relates to the estimates that are
required to consider the future total costs of the program and, thus,
to the relationship between these costs and the financing of the program. The second relates to our lack of knowledge, even our ignorance, about a number of the characteristics of the health care
system, utilization, and financing as these exist today." In the
third section, financial equity and distributional elements are examined such that "...we are reminded that the consideration of
equity should involve the proportion of medical care expenditures that would and would not be income related, as well as
the nature of the tax mechanism that would finance those expenditures which are viewed as related to the individual or
family income status. Furthermore, because the payment mechanism represents only one part of the equation that we are
interested in, we must consider the distribution of benefits."
A fourth section examines seven specific NHI proposals in the
context of financial equity and distribution of benefits.

See also:

(1) Pauly, Mark V. "Discussion of Fein Paper." NATIONAL
HEALTH INSURANCE, pp. 104-15.

(2) Lynch, Michael. "Discussion of Fein Paper." NATIONAL
HEALTH INSURANCE, pp. 117-21.

3.6 Feldstein, Martin S. "An Economic Model of the Medicare System."
QUARTERLY JOURNAL OF ECONOMICS 85 (February 1971): 1-20.

A. C^S, HK, PK

B. Appropriate allocation of resources in our highly decentral-
ized and mixed public-private health sector requires a general
understanding and specific estimates of the basic behavioral relations in the health care sector. Feldstein seeks to contribute "to the development of such an overall model of the
health sector by presenting a system of equations focusing on
the allocation of health care resources to the 20 million aged

persons under the Medicare program." It was found that: "Despite uniform and quite comprehensive health insurance of the aged population, very great variation remains in the use and benefits under the Medicare program. This paper has presented an econometric model of the Medicare subsystem that explains substantial portions of this variation in terms of demographic and economic characteristics of the population, state health policy variables, and characteristics of the local health care system." Furthermore, the author concluded that: "Uniform comprehensive insurance for the aged is not an appropriate policy when states differ in the availability of resources and the pattern of competing demands....In short, the econometric model of the Medicare system shows the importance of a more spatially disaggregated approach to health care policy. This lesson no doubt extends beyond Medicare to other public programs of health insurance and health care."

C. Empirical, quantitative methods

See also:

(1) Russell, Louise B. "An Econometric Model of the Medicare System." QUARTERLY JOURNAL OF ECONOMICS 87 (August 1973): 482-89.

(2) Feldstein, Martin S. "An Econometric Model of the Medicare System." QUARTERLY JOURNAL OF ECONOMICS 87 (August 1973): 490-94.

3.7 _____. "The Welfare Loss of Excess Health Insurance." JOURNAL OF POLITICAL ECONOMY 81 (March/April 1973): 251-80.

A. C^S, $P^S F$, FK

B. The purpose of this paper is to analyze in detail the economics of health insurance. The first two sections specify and estimate a structural demand equation for health insurance. The parameter estimates indicate that an increase in the price of hospital care causes a substantial increase in the demand for insurance. The interrelationship between the purchase of insurance and the demand for/supply of hospital care is then examined. "There is mutually reinforcing behavior: more insurance increases the price of care, and a higher price of care increases the demand for insurance. Although the system is dynamically stable (nonexplosive), the interdependence between insurance and the price of care implies that there is more insurance and a higher price of care than would otherwise prevail. This interdependence also increases the effect of changes in any exogenous variables on both the price of care and the level of insurance." Estimates of welfare gains that would result from decreasing insurance by raising the average coinsurance rate from 0.33 to 0.50 or 0.67 are then developed. It is determined that "the utility loss from increased risk would be more than outweighed by the gain due to lower prices and the reduced purchase of excess care....The most likely values imply net gains in excess of $4 billion." A final section suggests a way out of the current dilemma and relates to a general restructuring of the form of health insurance.

C. Quantitative methods

3.8   Friedman, Bernard. "Consumer Response to Incentives under Alternative Health Insurance Programs." INQUIRY 10 (September 1973): 31-35.

A. FK

B. "This paper [presents] some general discussion of the economics of an improved health insurance system. Special attention is given to an argument that the complete elimination of copayment formulae in health insurance would yield social gains from earlier treatment of serious illness, and that these gains would outweigh the losses due to unwarranted utilization." [The reference here is to Feldstein's article, "The Welfare Loss of Excess Health Insurance," entry 3.7.] It is concluded that, in general, for families at both the high end and the low end of the expenditure distribution, "...important reductions of family financial risk can be achieved through a lower maximum copayment in the event of 'catastrophic' losses. This change in coverage can be expected to generate inflationary pressures on costs of medical care which would require more formalized non-price rationing. At the lower end of the expenditure distribution, the complete elimination of copayment does not seem to be the answer to shortening the delay between appearance of symptoms and treatment for serious illness."

3.9   Fuchs, Victor R. "Impact of National Health Insurance Plans on Costs: A Framework for Determination." In NATIONAL HEALTH INSURANCE, Proceedings of the conference on National Health Insurance held November 1970, University of Pennsylvania, edited by Robert D. Eilers and Sue S. Moyerman, pp. 184-98. Homewood, Ill.: Richard D. Irwin, 1971.

A. $P^S F$

B. "The specific purpose of this paper is to compare the cost implications of seven plans for national health insurance" [AMA Medicredit proposal, Rockefeller Bill, Javits Bill, Griffiths Bill, Kennedy Bill (Committee for National Health Insurance)]. To provide an introductory base, three subjects are briefly discussed--concepts of cost, a framework for analysis, and recent expenditure patterns. "The main body of the paper discusses the implications of each plan with respect to the major determinants of cost. These determinants are health status, the incentives and constraints facing patients and physicians, productivity, factor prices, and administrative overhead." Fuchs concludes his analysis with the following: "Probably the most important conclusion...is that it is impossible to estimate what any of them [the 7 plans] will cost within a confidence range that can be useful to planners or legislators...[and] that we should favor proposals that place the physician in a position where he will have both the desire and the ability to control cost."

See also:

(1) Feldstein, Martin S. "Discussion of Fuchs Paper." NATIONAL HEALTH INSURANCE, pp. 201-7.

(2) Fuchs, Victor R. "Reply to Feldstein's Comments." NATIONAL HEALTH INSURANCE, pp. 208-9.

(3) Edelson, Noel M. "Discussion of Fuchs Paper." NATIONAL HEALTH INSURANCE, pp. 210-17.

3.10 Garbarino, Joseph W. HEALTH PLANS AND COLLECTIVE BARGAINING. Berkeley and Los Angeles: University of California Press, 1960. 301 p.

A. HK, FK

B. "This study [is] concerned with one part of the private wage supplement system, the provision of hospital and medical care through collectively bargained health plans. Emphasis [is] upon the fact that these collectively bargained health plans are part of a massive attempt to meet an important social problem through a voluntary, privately administered program....It [is] shown that the inclusion of medical care as an issue in contract negotiations has substantially increased the speed of an evolution in the conditions under which medical services are performed and, in addition, has turned this evolution into new channels....In chapter ii the structure of the medical market is examined...to assess the position of the collectively bargained health plans in the medical market....In chapter iii attention is shifted to the functioning of the medical market.... The focus in this chapter is on the degree of inflation of the prices of medical care and the forces that might account for the observed price behavior. In chapter iv the problem of the abuse of health insurance is examined. The next four chapters examine the way in which the labor movement in the San Francisco Bay Area has attempted to utilize its bargaining position in relation to the medical industry and the insuring agencies to deal with the cost problems of health plans....Chapter ix concerns itself with a series of special problems, some of general significance, which have characterized the past decade of health plan developments in the local area. Chapter x attempts to assess the implications of the experience reported in this study for the future of private and public health insurance and chapter xi discusses the role that labor-management plans are to play in that future."

3.11 Hester, James, and Leveson, Irving. "The Health Insurance Study: A Critical Appraisal." INQUIRY 11 (March 1974): 53-60.

A. C^S, P^S

B. The authors' "main concern is how well the experiment can provide reliable information on changes in patterns of use, cost and quality of medical care that accompany major changes in demand without exploring responses of the total health care system supplying those services." They are convinced that the experiment cannot provide adequate information on these matters, and the following elements are basic to their viewpoint: (1) changes in the supply of manpower and facilities need to be considered; (2) supply and demand elasticities may differ depending on the policy toward rate regulation that is followed; (3) consideration needs to be given to how changes in the degree of insurance coverage might influence the intensity and quality of care; (4) the "implications of a national financing plan for redistribution of demand among providers make the supply system response to alternative plans a crucial issue"; and (5) given a large-scale, long-term change in demand, there is a tendency for new methods of producing and delivering services to develop. Basically, Hester and Leveson conclude that if supply system response and regulation are accepted as key aspects of the experiment, then three to five years is an insufficient period of time, and the sample size is too small.

See also:

(1) Newhouse, Joseph P. "A Design for a Health Insurance Experiment." INQUIRY 11 (March 1974): 5-27.

(2) Newhouse, Joseph P. "The Health Insurance Study: Response to Hester and Leveson." INQUIRY 11 (September 1974): 236-41.

> Here, Newhouse notes that the critical appraisal by Hester and Leveson is based on a crucial misconception--"namely, that the experiment was designed to replicate what would happen if various health insurance proposals were enacted into law... ....[The] experiment [states Newhouse] is not a 'pilot' national health insurance plan. Nor is it a 'field trial' of any proposed legislation. Rather, it is designed to estimate [in part] how various insurance plans affect the demand for medical care and the health status of individuals..." In this communication, the author considers "first the usefulness of the experimental data if a national plan does not create stress on the delivery system, and then the usefulness if it does."

3.12 Hibbard, Thomas H. "Insurance and the Optimal Distribution of Medical Care." WESTERN ECONOMIC JOURNAL 9 (September 1971): 231-41.

A. FK

B. This paper critically examines Arrow's suggested nonprice demand controls--i.e., that the insurer, the physician, and the insured individual could restrain demand to the optimal level (Arrow. "The Economics of Moral Hazard: Further Comment." AMERICAN ECONOMIC REVIEW, June 1968). Section 1 shows that "the optimal distribution of medical care over an individual's health states is affected by the introduction of demand-controlled medical insurance." The second section "derives an expression for the optimal level of medical care under demand-controlled insurance in terms of variables about which some information exists. This expression is used to estimate the difference between optimal levels of care with and without demand-controlled insurance for some hypothetical individuals....The fundamental conclusion is that while such control mechanisms [Arrow's] may constitute a means of reaching the optimal level and distribution of medical care, they should not be used to duplicate the demand pattern that would have been forthcoming in the absence of insurance."

C. Quantitative methods, theoretical economics

3.13 Hill, Daniel B., and Veney, James E. "Kansas Blue Cross/Blue Shield Outpatient Benefits Experiment." MEDICAL CARE 8 (March/April 1970): 143-58.

A. C^S, FK

B. "A widely held, but unproven assumption holds that health insurance which financed more comprehensive services for ambulatory patients would significantly lower the rate of hospital admissions. This study reports on an attempt to test this assumption through a statistically controlled experiment. The Kansas Blue Cross/Blue Shield Plan provided free out-of-hospital benefits to an experimental group of 5,000 contracts for eight months during 1968. This group's inpatient claims experience was tested for significant changes by comparisons with prior experience and with a control group of 10,000 contracts. While the experimental benefits did not significantly alter the experimental group's total inpatient utilization rates, further analysis suggests that the benefits might have affected the distribution of inpatient care."

C. Empirical

3.14 Joseph, Hyman. "Hospital Insurance and Moral Hazard." JOURNAL OF HUMAN RESOURCES 7 (Spring 1972): 152-61.

A. C^S, P^S

B. "Cross-section [1965-66] data are used to determine the effect of third-party payments on the length of stay in [twenty-seven Iowa hospitals] for 22 separate illnesses or conditions, thereby providing a test of the effect of third-party payments on resource allocation to hospitals. Also, estimates are made of price elasticities of demand for the separate illnesses or conditions. This study, by discovering patterns of behavior among medical categories that have been obscured in aggregate demand studies, has important implications regarding the existence and extent of 'moral hazard,' the effectiveness of coinsurance, and the effect of extended-care facilities on resource allocation."

3.15 Kaitz, Edward M. PRICING POLICY AND COST BEHAVIOR IN THE HOSPITAL INDUSTRY. New York: Frederick A. Praeger, Publishers, 1968. 192 p.

For annotation see 1.30.

3.16 Lave, Judith R.; Lave, Lester B.; and Silverman, Lester P. "A Proposal for Incentive Reimbursement for Hospitals." MEDICAL CARE 11 (March/April 1973): 79-90.

For annotation see 1.36.

3.17 MacIntyre, Duncan M. "Pricing Health Insurance." In THE ECONOMICS OF HEALTH AND MEDICAL CARE, Proceedings of a conference held May 1962, Ann Arbor, Mich., edited by S.J. Axelrod, pp. 148-69. Ann Arbor: University of Michigan Press, 1964.

A. FK

B. "This paper deals with health insurance rates, rating and rate making." The three sections are divided as follows: "The first introduces some of the problems connected with these topics and provides a background for understanding the discussion in the succeeding sections. The second attempts to explain why and how United States health insurance companies and prepayment plans have taken different approaches to rates and rate making and analyzes the differences in the rate-making and rating techniques used by these competing organizations. Stressed are the interrelationships between intercarrier competition, seller benefit, underwriting and pricing techniques, and the attitudes and proclivities of buyers. The concluding section contains an evaluation of different rate methods from the standpoint of private and public policy."

3.18 Moyerman, Sue S. "Appendix B: Summaries of National Health Insurance Plans." In NATIONAL HEALTH INSURANCE, Proceedings of the conference on National Health Insurance held November 1970, University of Pennsylvania, edited by Robert D. Eilers and Sue S. Moyerman, pp. 287-333. Homewood, Ill.: Richard D. Irwin, 1971.

A. FK

B. Seven national health insurance plans are summarized individually in the following format: (a) summary, (b) eligibility, (c) annual benefits, (d) financing, (e) management and adminis- tration, (f) organization and delivery of care, and (g) methods and rates of reimbursement. The seven plans are: The AMA's Medicredit plan, the Aetna plan, the Rockefeller plan, the Feldstein plan, the Javits plan, the Griffiths plan, and the Committee for National Health Insurance--Kennedy plan. In addition, three plans proposed after the conference are simi- larly summarized: the Health Insurance Association of America plan, the American Hospital Association's Ameriplan, and Presi- dent Nixon's National Health Insurance plan.

3.19 Newhouse, Joseph P. "A Design for a Health Insurance Experiment." INQUIRY 11 (March 1974): 5-27.

A. C^S, FK

B. "This paper discusses the design of the experimental por- tion of the Health Insurance Study." This federally funded, $32 million experiment to be carried out by the RAND Cor- poration was begun in 1974. "The broad aim of the study is to improve the formulation of public policy in health care fi- nancing. To do this, several research objectives are being pursued": (1) exploring how the demand for medical services varies with the price the consumer must pay; (2) measuring the effect of various financing provisions on the demand for medical services; (3) establishing the effect of financing pro- visions on health status; (4) exploring administrative proce- dures concerning health insurance; (5) addressing the effects of HMO's on both utilization and health status; and (6) measuring the effects of the varying workloads of physicians in different communities. Each objective is discussed individually and, in subsequent sections, these objectives are related to the design of this large-scale, long-term experiment. A summary table is pro- vided regarding the experiment's principal dimensions.

C. Descriptive

See also:

(1) Orr, Larry L. "The Health Insurance Study: Experimenta- tion and Health Financing Policy." INQUIRY 11 (March 1974): 28-39.

> The author provides a rationale for spending $32 million in federal funds on this experiment. His "paper may signal a changing government perspec- tive on the production of knowledge in social re- search." (Quoted from J.E. Veney's introduction to the March, 1974 issue of INQUIRY.)

(2) Hester, James, and Leveson, Irving. "The Health Insurance Study: A Critical Appraisal." (entry 3.11)

3.20 Pauly, Mark V. "The Economics of Moral Hazard: Comment." THE AMERICAN ECONOMIC REVIEW 58 (June 1968): 531-37.

A. C^S, FK

B. Using as a point of reference Arrow's "Uncertainty and the Welfare Economics of Medical Care" (entry G.4), Pauly argues that "even if all individuals are risk-averters, insurance against some types of uncertain events may be nonoptimal. Hence, the fact that certain kinds of insurance have failed to emerge in the private market may be no indication of non-optimality, and compulsory government insurance against some uncertain events may lead to inefficiency. It [is] also shown that the problem of 'moral hazard' in insurance has, in fact, little to do with morality, but can be analyzed with orthodox economic tools." A theoretical approach is developed and related to full insurance coverage, deductibles, and coinsurance.

See also:

(1) Arrow, Kenneth J. "The Economics of Moral Hazard: Further Comment." AMERICAN ECONOMIC REVIEW 58 (June 1968): 537-39.

In this brief note, Arrow accepts Pauly's convincing demonstration that the optimality of complete insurance is no longer valid when the method of insurance influences the demand for the services provided by the insurance policy. Consistent with his 1963 article, however, he again argues that: "Nonmarket controls, whether internalized as moral principles or externally imposed, are to some extent essential for efficiency."

(2) Crew, Michael. "Coinsurance and the Welfare Economics of Medical Care." AMERICAN ECONOMIC REVIEW 59 (December 1969): 906-8.

The Arrow ("Uncertainty and the Welfare Economics of Medical Care," entry G.4) and Pauly ("The Economics of Moral Hazard: Comment," entry 3.20) articles are used as the basis for this note. Crew attempts to outline an apparent paradox: "Where monopoly or some restriction of competition exists in the servicing of liability claims, coinsurance may lead to a Pareto optimal situation. Using the assumption of competition in the supply of medical care, it is possible to show that, because of the presence of the phenomenon known as 'moral hazard,' an optimal situation will not be attained under schemes of insurance or coinsurance."

3.21 Pauly, Mark V., and Drake, David F. "Effect of Third-Party Methods of Reimbursement on Hospital Performance." In EMPIRICAL STUDIES IN

HEALTH ECONOMICS, edited by Herbert Klarman, pp. 297-314. Baltimore: Johns Hopkins Press, 1970.

For annotation see 1.52.

3.22 Robertson, Robert L. "Comparative Medical Care Use Under Prepaid Group Practice and Free Choice Plans: A Case Study." INQUIRY 9 (September 1972): 70-76.

A. C^S

B. "This is a report of a study of utilization patterns under two different coverage and organizational options. Specifically, it identifies and interprets differences in the use of medical services during an academic year between: a) public school teachers covered by a prepaid group practice program with comprehensive benefits (...'group program'); and b) teachers in the same community subscribing to an extensive nonprofit plan (...'blue plan')." Four hypotheses were tested. "Briefly put, these are that the group practice program, compared to the blue plan, will have: 1) a lower rate of inpatient admissions for surgical cases; 3) a lower rate of use of hospital patient days, medical and surgical; and 4) a high rate of outpatient physician contacts for medical cases....[The] general conclusions of the study are clear enough. There are savings of the prepaid group practice over the blue plan in terms of hospitalization and certain surgical care, advantages that are attributable more to organizational characteristics than to breadth of benefit coverage. Greater use of outpatient care by group program subscribers, perhaps induced by coverage differences, also is in evidence. These results...support proposals for private and public policies to promote group practice with capitation rather than simply to increase the scope of services prepaid."

3.23 Rosett, R.N., and Huang, Lien-fu. "The Effect of Health Insurance on the Demand for Medical Care." JOURNAL OF POLITICAL ECONOMY 81 (March/April 1973): 281-305.

A. C^S

B. "Data from the 1960 Survey of Consumer Expenditures are used to estimate price and income elasticities of the demand for hospitalization and physicians' services. The price elasticity ranges from -0.35 to -1.5 for prices ranging from 20 to 80 percent of the 1960 market price. The income elasticity ranges from 0.25 to 0.45 for incomes ranging from $4,000 to $10,000. The estimated demand function is used to calculate the cost of providing protection against the highly probable, small losses typically covered by health insurance policies. A family with an income of $7,000 paid 2.5 times the actuarial value of the loss to protect itself against a highly probable $110 loss."

C. Empirical, quantitative methods

3.24 Russell, Louise B. "The Impact of the Extended-Care Facility Benefit on Hospital Use and Reimbursements Under Medicare." JOURNAL OF HUMAN RESOURCES 8 (Winter 1973): 57-72.

For annotation see 1.64.

3.25 Vogel, Ronald J., and Morrall, John F. III. "The Impact of Medicaid on State and Local Health and Hospitals Expenditures, with Special Reference to Blacks." JOURNAL OF HUMAN RESOURCES 8 (Spring 1973): 202-11.

For annotation see 4.9.

3.26 Weiss, Jeffrey H., and Brodsky, Lynda. "An Essay on the National Financing of Health Care." JOURNAL OF HUMAN RESOURCES 7 (Spring 1972): 139-51.

A. C^S, P^S

B. "Proposed plans for the national financing of health care seek to eliminate the problems of a maldistribution of health services and resources, an inefficient medical care delivery system, rapidly rising costs and prices, and inadequate catastrophic health insurance." Subsequent to a discussion integrating these problems with the mechanism of national health insurance, four insurance-based objectives are identified, and the authors note: "Because these objectives cannot be advanced simultaneously, one must decide on an ordering of objectives. After priorities are established, many issues such as eligibility requirements, benefits covered, reimbursement rules, financing mechanisms, and administration remain to be decided. Senator Kennedy's Health Security program is used to illustrate the trade-off effects of the provisions of one plan against the objectives of national health insurance."

Chapter 5

PUBLIC HEALTH, DISEASE/ILLNESS-SPECIFIC ANALYSES,
INTERNATIONAL HEALTH

A. PUBLIC HEALTH

4.1   Bailey, Richard M. "Economics and Planning." In NOTES ON COM-
      PREHENSIVE PLANNING FOR HEALTH, edited by Henrik L. Blum and
      Associates, pp. 9.01-9.45. Berkeley: Comprehensive Health Planning
      Unit, School of Public Health, University of California, 1968.

      For annotation see 6.57.

4.2   Culyer, A.J. "Medical Care and the Economics of Giving." ECONOM-
      ICA 38 (August 1971): 295-303.

      For annotation see G.14.

4.3   Fein, Rashi. "Health Programs and Economic Development." In THE
      ECONOMICS OF HEALTH AND MEDICAL CARE, Proceedings of a con-
      ference held May 1962, Ann Arbor, Mich., edited by S.J. Axelrod, pp.
      271-82. Ann Arbor: University of Michigan Press, 1964.

      A. HK

      B. An integration of health measures, population, and econom-
      ic development is the theme of this generalized paper. Ini-
      tially, the resource "labor" is discussed in itself and in a his-
      torical perspective (specifically, development of the human
      capital concept). Next, a method for computing the money
      value of a man to society is examined. Given this background,
      health measures, population, and economic growth are inte-
      grated in the context of developing countries. Essentially,
      Fein suggests that "those who quickly say that health expendi-
      tures make the problem worse may be wrong." It is important
      to understand, however, that health improvement is "part of a
      much larger complex and cannot be considered in vacuo. The
      economist, concerned about human resources and economic
      development, must know more about the public health measures
      to be taken and their demographic implications just as the pub-

lic health expert must know the impact that the measures he advances will have on the economy."

See also:

Goode, Richard. "Comment." ECONOMICS OF HEALTH, pp. 282-85.

> In his comments, Goode emphasizes Fein's efforts to disentangle the population question from the size of the labor force. "He [Fein] shows succinctly and persuasively that health programs may increase the size of the effective labor force more than they increase the population."

4.4 Lindsay, Cotton M. "Medical Care and the Economics of Sharing." ECONOMICA 36 (November 1969): 351-62.

For annotation see G.39.

4.5 Paglin, Morton. "Public Health and Development: A New Analytical Framework." ECONOMICA 41 (November 1974): 432-41.

A. C^S, P^S

B. The main purpose of the model presented here is to integrate "public health as a consumer good into the theory of consumer choice and welfare, thus making life expectancy gains comparable to gains in real product. While frequent reference will be made to public health work, the theory presented here encompasses all types of health expenditures. However, as the model is applied to the evaluation of health programmes in underdeveloped areas, we emphasize the public health component of health expenditures, since a large part of the population in these countries receives health services mainly from medical and para-medical public health workers...stress is placed on the differences between the dominant 'public health as an investment' approach and the theory of health as a consumer good which is developed here."

C. Theoretical

4.6 Perlman, Mark. "Some Economic Aspects of Public Health Programs in Underdeveloped Areas." In THE ECONOMICS OF HEALTH AND MEDICAL CARE, Proceedings of a conference held May 1962, Ann Arbor, Mich., edited by S.J. Axelrod, pp. 286-99. Ann Arbor: University of Michigan Press, 1964.

A. P^S

B. "This paper is concerned with the significance of public health programs for regional or national economic development. One purpose is to review aspects of the economic development involved in public health administration. Another is to consider the currently popular view that expenditure on such administration per force impedes economic development because

such expenditures leads to overpopulation....In this discussion...
it is assumed that public health programs can contain provisions
to restrain undesired population growth. Three questions are
posed in this essay:

> 1. What principal characteristics must public health
> programs have if they are to aid regional or national
> economic development significantly?

> 2. What criteria should be employed in determining
> the composition of public health programs for select-
> ed areas?

> 3. What are the principles of finance which public
> health administrators should consider in planning their
> programs?"

See also:

Ruderman, A. Peter. "Comment." ECONOMICS OF HEALTH,
pp. 299-305.

4.7 Piore, Nora. "Metropolitan Areas and Public Medical Care." In THE
ECONOMICS OF HEALTH AND MEDICAL CARE, Proceedings of a conference held May 1962, Ann Arbor, Mich., edited by S.J. Axelrod,
pp. 60-70. Ann Arbor: University of Michigan Press, 1964.

A. C^S, P^S

B. "This paper deals with...one component of the medical
care economy of our cities, i.e., health and medical services
provided or purchased by government." Data from a New York
City-based project are used as the empirical base for this project. As noted in the "Comment" which follows this paper,
Mrs. Piore develops three major points: (1) public funds pay
for over one-third of all the health care received by New York
City residents; (2) well-planned and coordinated action could
yield a greater return on the public investment in health care;
(3) such planned and coordinated action in the public sector
could lead to higher efficiency in the whole private-public
health care establishment.

See also:

Lampman, Robert J. "Comment." ECONOMICS OF HEALTH,
pp. 71-74.

4.8 Siebert, Calvin D. "Benefit-Cost Analysis and Public Health Expenditures:
A Survey." Bureau of Business and Economic Research, College of Business Administration. Working Paper Series no. 71-12. Iowa City: University of Iowa, 1971. 51 p.

A. P^S

B. "The purpose of this paper is to consider the theoretical

basis of benefit-cost analysis and the special problems associated with its applications. With this background, [the author]
selectively critique[s] applications of benefit-cost analysis to
the health field. The next section develops the theoretical
framework for the application of benefit-cost analysis and the
pragmatic adjustments which are needed to apply it in an im-
perfectly competitive economy. Such problems as redistribution
effects and information costs are considered. In the third section, selected actual and proposed applications of benefit-cost
analysis to health programs are critiqued, employing the general framework developed in the previous section. The paper
closes with some general comments about future application of
benefit-cost analysis in the health field."

4.9   Vogel, Ronald J., and Morrall, John F. III. "The Impact of Medicaid
      on State and Local Health and Hospitals Expenditures, with Special Refer-
      ence to Blacks." JOURNAL OF HUMAN RESOURCES 8 (Spring 1973):
      202-11.

      A. C^S, P^S, FK

      B. "A simple demand and supply model is proposed to 'explain'
      the wide variations in state and local government expenditures
      on health and hospitals, and to assess the impact of Medicaid
      in satisfying the health needs of blacks. The model shows
      that a large percentage of variation can be explained and that
      blacks tend to demand and evidently receive a higher propor-
      tion of public health care on the basis of their income than
      one would expect. The discriminatory effects of Medicare are
      more than offset by a combination of Medicaid and state and
      local spending on health care, although the continuing racial
      health gap indicates that state and local spending has not off-
      set the wide differences between blacks and whites in private
      and Medicare spending."

4.10 Weisbrod, Burton A. ECONOMICS OF PUBLIC HEALTH. Philadelphia:
      University of Pennsylvania Press, 1961. 127 p.

      A. P^S

      B. The general intent herein is to apply cost-benefit analysis
      in the area of public health. Specifically, a procedure is
      developed--and subsequently applied to cancer, tuberculosis,
      and poliomyelitis--as an aid in making rational choices among
      alternative public health projects. The theme of resource-
      allocation decisions, explicit and implicit throughout the
      entries in this bibliography, is here given explicit treatment.

      C. Empirical, methodological

4.11 Weisbrod, B[urton].A.; Andreano, R.L.; Baldwin, R.E.; Epstein, E.H.; and
      Kelley, A.C. DISEASES AND ECONOMIC DEVELOPMENT, THE IM-

PACT OF PARASITIC DISEASES IN ST. LUCIA. Madison: University of Wisconsin Press, 1973. 218 p.

For annotation see 5.9

B. DISEASE/ILLNESS-SPECIFIC ANALYSES

5.1 Klarman, H[erbert].E.; Francis, J. O'S.; and Rosenthal, G[erald].D. "Cost Effectiveness Analysis Applied to the Treatment of Chronic Renal Disease." MEDICAL CARE 6 (January/February 1968): 48–54.

A. P^SF

B. "This paper attempts to answer one question: Under existing conditions of knowledge regarding the cost and end-results of treating patients with chronic renal disease, what is the best mix of center dialysis, home dialysis, and kidney transplantation? The question is explored through the application of cost-effectiveness analysis." It is concluded that "transplantation is economically the most effective way to increase the life expectancy of persons with chronic kidney disease."

C. Empirical

5.2 McCaffree, Kenneth M. "The Economic Basis for the Development of Community Mental Health Programs." MEDICAL CARE 6 (July/August 1968): 286–99.

A. P^SPK, F

B. "...[The] economic efficiency of community activities, represented by treatment in psychiatric wards of general hospitals and in day treatment centers, is examined and compared with the effectiveness and costs of acute-treatment services of a state mental hospital." A prerequisite to this efficiency analysis is first discussed--i.e., the actual identification of the product (of mental health care) and associated costs. Three specific mental health care settings are then examined and compared, with these qualified results: Average per-patient direct costs were less in the day treatment center and in the psychiatric ward of the general hospital than in the state mental hospital. A "major portion of the treatment program in the psychiatric ward of the general hospital appears preferable, on comparative-costs bases, to the treatment program in the state mental hospital....Finally, it should be recognized that the three types of institutions for the mentally ill are supplementary, to a degree, and are not substitutes for one another. In conclusion, the economic basis for preferring community mental health programs to state mental hospitals depends upon one or the other, or both, of two propositions. First, the community programs serve a group of persons not now being cared for by the state mental hospital....Second, the more intensive care and shorter period of disability associated with the inpatient-outpatient pattern of care through the psychiatric wards of the general hospital provides lower total (direct plus indirect) costs of mental illness than alternative treatment programs in the other types of institutions."

C. Empirical

5.3 Rice, Dorothy P. ESTIMATING THE COST OF ILLNESS. Health Economics Series no. 6. U.S. Department of Health, Education, and Welfare-- Public Health Service Publication no. 947-6. Washington, D.C.: Government Printing Office, 1966. 131 p.

A. HK

B. "This [three-part] study presents a framework for calculating the economic costs of illness, disability and death and performs the calculations. Part I discusses the problems involved in measuring annual direct costs of illness, describes the procedures adopted, and presents data for selected types of health expenditures in 1963 by diagnosis. The second part deals with the annual indirect losses associated with illness, disability and death. Included are the economic concepts, estimating procedures and estimates of the total man-years lost and productivity losses resulting from morbidity and mortality in 1963 for each diagnostic category. The third part presents the methodology and resulting estimates of the present value of the future earnings for those people who died in 1963."

C. Empirical

5.4 Scheffler, Richard M., and Lipscomb, Joseph. "Alternative Estimations of Population Health Status: An Empirical Example." INQUIRY 11 (September 1974): 220-28.

A. HK

B. In the development of health status indices, there have been few attempts to consider simultaneously the pecuniary and nonpecuniary dimensions of disease. "The purpose of this paper is to show--by means of an empirical example--how sample survey data indicating both the prevalence of disability and its economic consequences can become the crucial input into alternative health status indices. One index will be seen to reflect the physiological-emotional cost, and the other, the monetary cost of disability." Using data on health status and income loss due to illness--derived from the Survey of Economic Opportunity, a national survey conducted in 1967 by the Bureau of the Census--and a panel of judges to rank health states according to utility, the authors argue that "the expected pecuniary benefits of disease programs, which have traditionally been measured in aggregative fashion by cost-benefit analysis, can be estimated in a form which makes them more comparable to the expected physiological-emotional benefits of programs..."

C. Quantitative methods

5.5 Scitovsky, Anne A. "Changes in the Costs of Treatment of Selected Ill-nesses, 1951-65." AMERICAN ECONOMIC REVIEW 57 (December 1967): 1182-95.

A. C^S

B. The author previously demonstrated the feasibility of develop-ing a medical care price index based on the average costs of treatment of specific illnesses (Scitovsky, entry 5.6). Here, Scitovsky estimates such average costs in five illness categories. Two different time periods (1951-52, 1964-65) were selected, and their determined cost changes were subsequently compared to the Bureau of Labor Statistics medical care price index. The BLS index is computed using selected items of medical care, and it measures only price changes (holding quantity and quali-ty constant). Except for one minor item, the average costs of all five illnesses increased more than the BLS index. Develop-ment of this cost-per-episode-of-illness approach was not viewed as a substitute for the current BLS index; rather it is suggested as an additional index "prepared every few years for purpose of comparison and evaluation of the present index."

See also:

(1) Barzel, Yoram. "Costs of Medical Treatment: Comment." AMERICAN ECONOMIC REVIEW 58 (September 1968): 936-38.

(2) Scitovsky, Anne. "Costs of Medical Treatment: Reply." AMERICAN ECONOMIC REVIEW 58 (September 1968): 938-40.

5.6 _____. "An Index of the Cost of Medical Care--A Proposed New Ap-proach." In THE ECONOMICS OF HEALTH AND MEDICAL CARE, Pro-ceedings of a conference held May 1962, Ann Arbor, Mich., edited by S.J. Axelrod, pp. 128-42. Ann Arbor: University of Michigan Press, 1964.

A. P^SF

B. "It is the purpose of this paper to review briefly the main shortcomings of the present medical care price index, to de-scribe a different approach to constructing such an index which would use specific illnesses rather than items of medical ser-vice as the unit to be priced, and to discuss the advantages which this approach would have over the present medical care price index." Substitution of "new for old" is not advocated "at this stage"; rather, comparisons over time should be made.

See also:

Reid, Margaret G. "Comment." ECONOMICS OF HEALTH, pp. 142-47.

5.7 Weisbrod, Burton A. "Costs and Benefits of Medical Research: A Case Study of Poliomyelitis." JOURNAL OF POLITICAL ECONOMY 79 (May/June 1971): 527-44.

A. FK

B. "The paper provides estimates of (1) research expenditures on poliomyelitis, (2) several forms of productivity benefits from applying the knowledge generated by the research, and (3) the costs of applying that knowledge. Internal rates of return are computed under a variety of assumptions, with results generally between 4 and 14 percent. The interrelatedness of research with procedures for applying the research findings is investigated; in the case of polio, the rate of return on research is found to be heavily influenced by the costs of application. Finally, a discussion is included of the likely allocative efficiency of private-market behavior when a collective-consumption good, such as research knowledge, requires the use of an individual-consumption good, such as a vaccination, for its application."

See also:

Holtmann, A.G. "On the Optimal Timing of Research Expenditures." (Research Report) INQUIRY 10 (March 1973): 47-49.

Using data from Weisbrod's study, "the optimization rules for the completion of a medical research project are related, and the level and time pattern of expenditures made in the case of polio are examined." In a generalized context, Holtmann is attempting to stimulate research regarding the "relationship between the speed of a research project and its cost..."

5.8 _____. ECONOMICS OF PUBLIC HEALTH. Philadelphia: University of Pennsylvania Press, 1961. 127 p.

For annotation see 4.10.

5.9 Weisbrod, B[urton].A.; Andreano, R.L.; Baldwin, R.E.; Epstein, E.H.; and Kelley, A.C. DISEASE AND ECONOMIC DEVELOPMENT, THE IMPACT OF PARASITIC DISEASES IN ST. LUCIA. Madison: University of Wisconsin Press, 1973. 218 p.

A. HK

B. "Our objective...is to set forth and then to implement a

systematic approach for examining--quantitatively, to the extent possible--the economic and social impacts of disease....
Our empirical work is concentrated on the effects of schistosomiasis, but to discover these effects involves controlling for
the influence of other diseases....Thus, efforts have [also] been
made to assess the impacts of...hookworm, Ascaris, Trichuris,
and Strongyloides....The format for...this book is as follows:
after surveying previous research on the relationships between
health and economic development in chapter 2, we will present...information about...St. Lucia, and our case-study disease, schistosomiasis, in chapters 3 and 4. Chapter 5 and
Appendices B, C, and D are devoted to quantitative assessment of the effects of schistosomiasis and other parasitic diseases. Three types of disease impacts will be investigated:
demographic effects--influences on birth and death rates...
school-performance effects on children...and labor-productivity
effects....In chapters 6 and 7 we will discuss the meaning
and implication of our findings....Finally there are appendices
dealing with the representativeness of our data...with some
evidence on the labor-supply function in St. Lucia...and with
the possibility that economic development has itself served to
spread schistosomiasis in St. Lucia...."

C. INTERNATIONAL HEALTH

6.1 Cooper, Michael. "Economics of Need: The Experience of the British
Health Service." In THE ECONOMICS OF HEALTH AND MEDICAL
CARE, Proceedings of a conference held by the International Economic
Association, April 1973, Tokyo, edited by Mark Perlman, pp. 89-107.
New York: John Wiley and Sons, 1973.

A. C^S, $P^S L$

B. "Twenty-five years of employing 'need' as the main allocative device within the Health Service has demonstrated that
'need' is capable of almost infinite interpretation. In a zero-
price market no level of provision exists to eliminate excess
demand and remove the necessity for rationing. This rationing
function has never been explicitly recognized, but has fallen
by default upon the medical profession as the main decision-
makers of the Service. Doctors, however, have claimed the
complete clinical freedom to act solely in the interests of each
individual patient while being accountable only to their own
personal consciences. As a consequence, rationing has taken
place only implicitly, resulting in inconsistencies of medical
practice and in inequalities of provision. Further, need being
limitless, the Service has found it easier to claim shortages of
resources than to examine critically their current deployment.
A better understanding of the process by which the need for
medical care is determined and a re-examination of the rationality of clinical freedom is attempted."

See also:

"Summary Record of Discussion." ECONOMICS OF HEALTH, pp. 130-34.

6.2 Fein, Rashi. "Health Programs and Economic Development." In THE ECONOMICS OF HEALTH AND MEDICAL CARE, Proceedings of a conference held May 1962, Ann Arbor, Mich., edited by S.J. Axelrod, pp. 271-82. Ann Arbor: University of Michigan Press, 1964.

For annotation see 4.3.

6.3 Feldstein, Martin S. ECONOMIC ANALYSIS FOR HEALTH SERVICE EFFICIENCY. Chicago: Markham Publishing Co., 1968. 325 p.

A. C^S, P^S

B. "This study is concerned with identifying and estimating relevant decision-making information and with applying optimizing methods to improve the efficiency of the British National Health Service." Chapters 2-6 focus on the hospital as a producing unit and serve to illustrate public sector microeconomics. The remaining three chapters relate to a more aggregated level, focusing on the problems of planning the supply and use of health care resources.

C. Theoretical, empirical, quantitative methods

6.4 _____. "Health Sector Planning in Developing Countries." ECONOMICA 37 (May 1970): 139-63.

For annotation see 6.64.

6.5 Kleiman, Ephraim. "The Determinants of National Outlay on Health." In THE ECONOMICS OF HEALTH AND MEDICAL CARE, Proceedings of a conference held by the International Economic Association April 1973, Tokyo, edited by Mark Perlman, pp. 66-81. New York: John Wiley and Sons, 1973.

A. C^S

B. "This paper investigates international differences in per capita levels of health outlay and in their division between private and public components. The findings support the hypothesis that households, having decided on their desired level of outlays in view of their health conditions and their income, then adjust to allow for the provision of health services by the public sector. Similarly, it holds that the public sector behaves in a parallel manner, adjusting its level of outlays on health services to allow for qualities acquired privately by households. However, from the standpoint of each of the two sectors, the services provided by the other one are imperfect substitutes for those provided by itself."

C. Quantitative methods

See also:

"Summary Record of Discussion." ECONOMICS OF HEALTH, pp. 85–88.

6.6 Paglin, Morton. "Public Health and Development: A New Analytical Framework." ECONOMICA 41 (November 1974): 432–41.

For annotation see 4.5.

6.7 Perlman, Mark. "Some Economic Aspects of Public Health Programs in Underdeveloped Areas." In THE ECONOMICS OF HEALTH AND MEDI-CAL CARE, Proceedings of a conference held May 1962, Ann Arbor, Mich., edited by S.J. Axelrod, pp. 286–99. Ann Arbor: University of Michigan Press, 1964.

For annotation see 4.6.

6.8 Weisbrod, B[urton].A.; Andreano, R.L.; Baldwin, R.E.; Epstein, E.H.; and Kelley, A.C. DISEASE AND ECONOMIC DEVELOPMENT, THE IMPACT OF PARASITIC DISEASES IN ST. LUCIA. Madison: University of Wisconsin Press, 1973. 218 p.

For annotation see 5.9.

Chapter 6

GENERAL AND MISCELLANEOUS
HEALTH/MEDICAL SECTOR STUDIES

A. GENERAL

G.1 Altman, Stuart H. "The Structure of Nursing Education and Its Impact on Supply." In EMPIRICAL STUDIES IN HEALTH ECONOMICS, edited by Herbert Klarman, pp. 335-52. Baltimore: Johns Hopkins Press, 1970.

A. HK

B. "In this paper a comprehensive theory of the economic forces that influence nursing education [is] developed, with a view toward understanding what has motivated the dramatic changes in the structure of nursing education and what impact these changes are likely to have on the future supply of professional nurses." A second development involves an explanation of the monopsonistic structure of the labor market for nurses. (See "Comment" by W. Lee Hansen, EMPIRICAL STUDIES, pp. 353-56.)

C. Quantitative methods

G.2 Andersen, Ronald, and Anderson, Odin. A DECADE OF HEALTH SERVICES. Chicago: University of Chicago Press, 1967. 244 p.

A. C^S

B. "Three national surveys separated by five-year intervals give us a fair description of the consumer's use of medical care, the degree of his health insurance protection, and expenditures for care. Data so describing consumer behavior have been analyzed in detail in this report." The three surveys were taken in 1953, 1958, and 1963, a decade which bridges a period of sharp rise in medical care costs and health insurance benefits. "The findings are divided into five chapters. The first three treat consecutively people's use of health services, how much they are charged for these services, and how they go about paying for them. The next chapter considers some of the relationships among use, expenditure, and method of payment....The final section summarizes the findings and points out some implications of these results."

C. Empirical

G.3 Andersen, Ronald, and Benham, Lee. "Factors Affecting the Relationship between Family Income and Medical Care Consumption." In EMPIRICAL STUDIES IN HEALTH ECONOMICS, edited by Herbert Klarman, pp. 73-95. Baltimore: Johns Hopkins Press, 1970.

A. C^S

B. "The intent of this paper is to measure and assess the importance of some factors which may influence the relationship between family medical care consumption and family income." Regression analysis is used to examine the influence of five factor sets on observed income elasticities of demand for medical care: (1) the effects of price and quality of medical care, preventive care, and family demographic variables; (2) the substitution of permanent income for observed income as the measure of a family's resources; (3) the expected negative relationship between illness and transitory income; (4) the association between permanent income and illness; and (5) the employment of quantities of service rather than dollar expenditures. (See "Comment" by Michael Grossman, EMPIRICAL STUDIES, pp. 96-100.)

C. Empirical, quantitative methods

G.4 Arrow, Kenneth J. "Uncertainty and the Welfare Economics of Medical Care." AMERICAN ECONOMIC REVIEW 53 (December 1963): 941-73.

A. C^S, P^S

B. "This paper is...an exploratory and tentative study of the specific differentia of medical care. It is contended here that the special economic problems of medical care can be explained as adaptations to the existence of uncertainty in the incidence of disease and in the efficacy of treatment." The focus of Arrow's work is "the way the operation of the medical-care industry and the efficacy with which it satisfies the needs of society differ from a norm, if at all." (The norm is taken to be the operation of a competitive model.) It is argued that "virtually all of the special features of this industry stem from the prevalence of uncertainty [and] that the special structural characteristics of the medical-care market are largely attempts to overcome the lack of optimality due to the nonmarketability of the bearing of suitable risks and the imperfect marketability of information. These compensatory institutional changes...largely explain the observed non-competitive behavior of the medical-care market; behavior which, in itself, interferes with optimality. The social adjustment towards optimality thus puts obstacles in its own path." The failure of the market to ensure against uncertainties has created many social institutions in which the usual assumptions of the market are to some extent contradicted.

C. Theoretical

See also:

(1) Lees, D.S., and Rice, R.G. "Comment." AMERICAN ECONOMIC REVIEW 55 (March 1965): 140-53.

(2) Arrow, K.J. "Reply." AMERICAN ECONOMIC REVIEW 55 (March 1965): 155-58.

(3) Boland, V.F. "Comment." AMERICAN ECONOMIC REVIEW 55 (December 1965): 1172-73.

G.5 Auster, Richard; Leveson, Irving; and Sarachek, Deborah. "The Production of Health, an Exploratory Study." In ESSAYS IN THE ECONOMICS OF HEALTH AND MEDICAL CARE, edited by V.R. Fuchs, pp. 135-58. New York: National Bureau of Economic Research, 1972.

A. C^S, P^S.

B. The authors' concern is with the impact of medical services on health. The "production process is [here] viewed as one that changes the health status of the population, [and therefore] medical services [are] considered as an intermediate product in the 'production of health'." The primary purpose is to estimate the elasticity of health with respect to medical services. Two models are developed: elasticity in Model I is determined through the measurement of per capita medical services expenditures. Model II assumes that the production function of medical services exhibits constant returns to scale and that an estimate of elasticity can be obtained by summing the coefficients of four variables--number of physicians per capita, number of paramedical personnel per capita, medical capital per capita, and prescription drug expenditures per capita. Age-adjusted 1960 death rates are used as the measure of health. "Both models indicate that a 1 per cent increase in the quantity of medical services is associated with a reduction in mortality of about 0.1 per cent. Environmental conditions are a more important determinant of interstate variation in death rates. Among these, income and education play the greatest role. The effect of income on mortality is positive while that of education is negative."

C. Theoretical, empirical, quantitative methods

G.6 Bailey, Richard M. "An Economist's View of the Health Services Industry." INQUIRY 6 (March 1969): 3-18.

A. C^S

B. The focus of this article is consumption theory (consumer demand for medical services) in the contexts of: (1) urgency of medical need; (2) price and income effects within "urgency of need" categories; (3) variations in the marketplace for health services and medical care. Included in this last context is a discussion of governmental involvement as a major and growing consumer; "health is a right" represents an important base for this discussion.

G.7 Barzel, Yoram. "Productivity and the Price of Medical Services." JOURNAL OF POLITICAL ECONOMY 77 (November/December 1969): 1014-27.

A. $P^S F$

B. The author argues that Consumer Price Index figures regarding the price of medical services "are a poor reflection of productivity change and that in fact the rate of increase of productivity in the medical services has exceeded somewhat the overall productivity increase in the rest of the economy." Given this CPI criticism, Barzel attempts to lay the foundation for the construction of a conceptually valid price index of medical services; his point of departure is the health insurance plan. Empirical data on health insurance for the years 1945-64 are used in an examination of the relationship between productivity and the price of medical services.

C. Empirical

G.8 Benham, Lee. "The Labor Market for Registered Nurses: A Three-Equation Model." REVIEW OF ECONOMICS AND STATISTICS 53 (August 1971): 246-52.

A. HK

B. "This study investigates factors influencing the number of employed registered nurses and their earnings across states. Several aspects of simultaneous response patterns in this labor market are examined by use of a simple model which includes one structural equation for demand, one for labor force participation, and one for geographical location." Specification of the structural equations is followed by empirical estimation (via three-stage least squares) using cross section 1950 and 1960 data. Reduced-form estimates, to measure net impact of the exogenous variables, are then developed. Given his results, the author suggests that his model can be used to examine the impact on the registered nurse market of such factors as "rising per capita income, falling birth rates, rising incomes of husbands of registered nurses, increases in the number of substitutes for registered nurses, and increases in the number of nursing schools."

C. Empirical, quantitative methods

G.9 Berkowitz, Monroe, and Johnson, William G. "Health and Labor Force Participation." JOURNAL OF HUMAN RESOURCES 9 (Winter 1974): 117-28.

A. HK

B. "Models are estimated to analyze the influence of health on labor force participation. It was found that the participation of blacks is more likely to be reduced by health factors than that of whites [and] that the primary importance of education derives from its association with skills and ability rather than health. Public transfer payments influence but do not control participation of nonseverely disabled workers. Including health measures can increase the explanatory power of labor force models. Better information on health of workers would allow separation of the cost of disability into those reducible through delivery of health care and those more appropriately dealt with through labor market policies."

G.10 Bognanno, M[ario].F.; Hixson, J.S.; and Jeffers, J[ames].R. "The Short-Run Supply of Nurse's Time." JOURNAL OF HUMAN RESOURCES 9 (Winter 1974): 80-94.

A. HK

B. "This study attempts to determine and explain the properties of the household's supply response to incentives offered by market demanders of nurses' services. With data obtained from individual households of married professional nurses, estimates are made of their supply response to changes in the wage rate and to changes in their husband's income, and of the impact of interhousehold differences on labor force behavior.... Analysis was conducted for two time periods [August-September 1968], and for each we estimated models to generate the probability of labor force participation and the expected amount of time worked, given participation. In contrast to the flow of labor supplied by employed married nurses, we find the participation decision is not dependent on the wage rate. Both dimensions of labor supply are dependent on [the] husband's earnings. The results also provide strong evidence that the supply curve is backward-bending just beyond the range of our observations."

C. Empirical, quantitative methods

G.11 Bognanno, Mario F., and Jeffers, James R. "Evidence on the Physician Shortage." Bureau of Business and Economic Research, College of Business Administration, Working Paper Series no. 71-13. Iowa City: University of Iowa, 1971. 39 p.

A. HK

B. The various methodologies and studies relating to the subject of physician shortages are reviewed in this working paper.

The concept of health manpower shortage is first examined and the matters of normative and economic shortages are discussed. Reference is then made to several normative empirical studies, followed by a compilation of criticisms relating to the normative and/or physician-to-population approach of estimating shortages. Factors which can cause the physician's productivity to increase are then noted--substituting cheaper inputs for physicians, changes in the organization of health care delivery, and the development of relatively costly labor-saving technology. Then Fein's approach (THE DOCTOR SHORTAGE, entry 2.5), Rayack's relative income approach, and Hansen's internal rate of return approach ("Shortages and Investment in Health Manpower," entry G.30) are examined. The authors conclude, in part, that: "Past studies do not provide a sound empirical basis for accepting the 'assertions' that in the aggregate there has been or will be physician shortages of a 'crisis' dimension....Two crucial components of any future study of physician shortages must be: (a) the inclusion of the concept of a generalized production function for physicians' services; and (b) the inclusion of national health insurance in the analysis of the demand for physicians' services."

G.12 Boulding, Kenneth. "The Concept of Need for Health Services." MILBANK MEMORIAL FUND QUARTERLY 44 (October 1966): 202-28.

A. P^S

B. Boulding here provides a far-ranging, general discussion of the medical need concept. Included in his "need framework" are: (1) professionally-determined or homeostatic need, as relating to individuals within a society; (2) an extension of homeostasis to society as a whole, where a distinction is made between public and societal health; and (3) need which derives from medical indigency, i.e., the needs of those who cannot demand a socially defined minimum of health care. The author stresses the importance of considering a multiple needs framework "in producing a system of medical care that compromises between needs and demands."

G.13 Culyer, A.J. "Is Medical Care Different?" In HEALTH ECONOMICS, SELECTED READINGS, edited by M.H. Cooper and A.J. Culyer, pp. 49-74. Baltimore: Penguin Books, 1973.

A. P^S

B. The purpose of this article, conceptual in its approach (extracted from Culyer's more extensive article in the OXFORD ECONOMICS PAPERS 23 [1971]: 189-211), is to attempt to resolve the difficulty of whether "the commodity 'health care' ...is different from other commodities in particular and crucial ways such as to make some forms of organization of the health industry intrinsically inefficient and others intrinsically efficient." Further, an attempt is made "to evaluate the policy implications that have been drawn for the appropriate organization of health care in terms of Pareto criterion..." Elements of consumer rationality, uncertainty and insurance, and externalities are examined, and it is asserted that "an itemization of its [health care's] characteristics tells us nothing about the most efficient method of producing or allocating it." A priori analysis, while necessary in the development of a "health care institutions" framework, needs to be complemented by empirical investigation of health care institutions. Two major implications derive from this summarily identified need for the application of positive economics: "(1) The first is that a far more extensive use of cost-effectiveness and cost-benefit analyses to improve extant institutions and to improve understanding of their general efficiency is required. (2) The second is that we need a well-developed positive theory of non-profit institutions from which implications comparable to those of the received theory of the firm can be derived."

G.14 _____. "Medical Care and the Economics of Giving." ECONOMICA 38 (August 1971): 295-303.

A. C^S, P^S

B. Using the Lindsay article on "the economics of sharing" (entry G.39) as a base, Culyer "seeks to reinstate the more traditional approach as a 'philanthropy' hypothesis in which it is the quantity of 'suffering' felt by people rather than the distribution of 'suffering' that forms the basis of the externality relation, and which affords a better explanation of the NHS [National Health Service]. In this paper the normative interpretation of Lindsay's theory will not be considered since a necessary condition for testing propositions in collective welfare economics (i.e., consensus decision-making) is clearly not fulfilled....For positive analysis, however, we might proceed faute de mieux on the assumption that collective decisions are made 'as if' this condition were fulfilled, or introduce modifications where appropriate. Granted this simplication, this paper makes two points (i) Any economic arrangement can be 'explained' by assuming that someone (or everyone) has a preference for it....(ii) An alternative characterization of utility functions can be devised which 'explains' the phenomena at least as well as Lindsay's theory (though still not perfectly)..."

C. Theoretical

See also:

Lindsay, Cotton M. "Medical Care and the Economics of Sharing." ECONOMICA 36 (November 1969): 351-62.

G.15 Fein, Rashi. "Medical Care Needs in the Coming Decade." BULLETIN

OF THE NEW YORK ACADEMY OF MEDICINE 45 (October 1969): 255-70.

A. C^S, P^S

B. The context of Fein's remarks is public policy and, specifically, with respect to the policy implications of needs projections. He is concerned with the kinds of projections that are most meaningful to those who can affect policy. He emphasizes that useful and meaningful projections can evolve only when that which is being projected is understood and accepted (e.g., agreement on what is meant by "met needs"). Benefit-cost analysis is discussed as a useful input into the decision-making process; and, in this measurement context, it is stressed that "the word need is intimately related to the concept of benefit." Furthermore, given this relationship between public policy and the projection of needs, it is noted that "for the guidance of public policy these needs must be translated into measures of the benefits that meeting them would bring." (This "translation" can take the form of benefit-cost ratios.) The paper concludes, first, with demand (not need) projections and then with fundamental guidelines for evaluating medical care actions in the coming decade.

G.16 _____. "On Achieving Access and Equity in Health Care." MILBANK MEMORIAL FUND QUARTERLY 50 (October 1972): 157-90.

A. C^S, P^S

B. The first question addressed is: "Why be concerned about equity?" Fein notes the distinction between medical care expenditures and both services (inputs) and health (output); then he discusses "the significance of the fact that the public believes the services to be important and, therefore, desires a greater equity in their distribution." Using this base, the subject of equity in access to care is considered, being divided into the areas of financial constraints and delivery system performance. The discussion on financial constraints includes the ability to pay for care and the impact of payment on family income and assets; equity-equality issues and present/future payment patterns are here considered. Delivery system performance is next considered, given that: (1) ultimately, costs will depend on how the system is structured and on physician behavior; and (2) even if financial barriers are removed, the distribution problem will not necessarily be solved through market adjustments. The area of delivery system performance is introduced with a discussion of the processes of regulation and market action. Next system issues are examined with special focus on the physician "because he is the critical actor in the health care system, because access to his services is a key equity issue and because, in large measure, he determines the utilization of other parts of the system." Topics included here are physician control of market forces, specialization and location, maldistribution, and alternatives to fee-for-service.

G.17 Fein, Rashi, and Weber, Gerald I. FINANCING MEDICAL EDUCATION, AN ANALYSIS OF ALTERNATIVE POLICIES AND MECHANISMS. New York: McGraw-Hill Book Co., for the Carnegie Commission on Higher Education and the Commonwealth Fund, 1971. 279 p.

A. HK, FK

B. In their introductory chapter, the authors provide the following format: "Our examination will address itself to financing: to the funds received and the funding structure. We shall analyze the manner in which the medical school is financed, the sources from which funds are received, and the uses to which they are put. We shall ask how these sources have changed over the years and how these movements have been associated with changes in the medical school itself. We shall pay particular attention to the roles that students, state governments, and the federal government might play in financing medical education, and we shall discuss alternative funding patterns and their implications. In undertaking these tasks we shall attempt to provide an analytical framework and a set of principles that can be used to assess relevant new data..."

C. Empirical

G.18 Feldstein, Paul J. "Research on the Demand for Health Services." MILBANK MEMORIAL FUND QUARTERLY 44 (July 1966): 128-62.

A. C^S, $P^S L$

B. "This paper [describes] an economic framework for explaining variations in the demand for health services. [Identification and measurement of] the relationship between use of a product or service and the factors influencing this use increases understanding of usage variations." Furthermore, the processes of specification and estimation are useful in both policy formation and in the related matter of predicting future demand. The framework set forth incorporates both the factors which affect patient demand for medical care and how the physician decides what components to use in administering services. Factors affecting patient demand for treatments include incidence of illness, cultural-demographic characteristics, and economic factors. Physician utilization of care components is determined by patient characteristics (including relative cost to the patient from using different components of care), institutional arrangements, physician's knowledge, and relative costs to the physician from using alternative sets of care components. A discussion of each of these factors is enhanced through reference to relevant empirical studies. This study is an effective nontechnical approach to the analysis of demand for health services.

G.19 Feldstein, Paul J., and Kelman, Sander. "A Framework for an Econometric Model of the Medical Care Sector." In EMPIRICAL STUDIES IN HEALTH ECONOMICS, edited by Herbert Klarman, pp. 171–90. Baltimore: Johns Hopkins Press, 1970.

A. C^S, P^S, HK

B. "The purposes of this paper...are to formulate a model of the medical care sector, to specify this model in equation form, to describe how the parameters for the equations were developed...." The model has three levels:

(1) The first level expresses the value of medical care as the sum of the values of said provided in each of the five institutional settings--hospitals, nursing homes, outpatient clinics, doctors' offices, and patient homes; it also includes the development of a Laspeyres price index based on this sum.

(2) Level two is an analysis of the supply of and demand for the services in these five settings.

(3) Finally, level three shows the derived health manpower demands and supply.

(See "Comment" by Peter E. deJanosi, EMPIRICAL STUDIES, pp. 191–94.)

C. Theoretical, quantitative methods

G.20 Fuchs, Victor R. "The Contribution of Health Services to the American Economy." MILBANK MEMORIAL FUND QUARTERLY 44 (October 1966): 65–101.

A. HK

B. This paper "does not pretend to offer a measure of the contribution of health services" to our economy. Its primary purpose "is to set out in nontechnical terms how the problem looks to an economist, to discuss definitions, concepts and methods of measurement, to indicate sources of information and to suggest promising research approaches." Fuchs first considers the meaning of contribution and asserts that it should be measured in terms of output and not input. Basically, he is then measuring the relative effect on health of a small relative change in health services. The next part--a discussion relating the effect of health services on health--is prefaced by a brief look at two interrelated concerns: (1) the definition of health and measurement of levels (changes in levels) of health; and (2) an examination of the problem of estimating what portion of changes in health can be attributed to health services, as distinct from the genetic and environmental factors that also affect health. Then, using this definition/measurement "problem perspective," an input-output analysis is set forth in which the effect of health services (input) is principally related to health (output). Finally, a "health and the economy" section is provided wherein direct (contributions to productive capacity) and indirect (changes in life attitudes which may accompany changes in health) effects of health services are examined.

G.21 _____. "The Growing Demand for Medical Care." In ESSAYS IN THE ECONOMICS OF HEALTH AND MEDICAL CARE, edited by V.R. Fuchs, pp. 61-68. New York: National Bureau of Economic Research, 1972.

A. C^S

B. Fuchs attempts to analyze the twenty-year, 8 percent average annual increase in medical care expenditures. His analysis of the factors contributing to the growth in expenditures for medical care, 1947-1967, includes: rise in the price of medical care (3.7%, 3.7%, 3.6%), population growth (1.6%, 1.8%, 1.5%), growth of real national income per capita (2.3%, 2.0%, 2.5%), and decline in quantity demanded because of rises in the relative price of medical care (-0.2%, -0.2%, -0.2%). The numbers in parenthesis represent percentages explained by that variable for the subperiods 1947-67, 1947-57, and 1957-67 respectively. For example, of the 8 percent average annual expenditures increase for 1947-67, a rise in the price of medical care explains 3.7 percent, population growth explains 1.6 percent, income growth explains 2.3 percent, etc. It is pointed out that the unexplained residual becomes more significant for the 1957-67 subperiod. Fuchs then examines this unexplained growth in demand, focusing on the impact of the physicians' "technologic imperative" approach (giving the best care that is technically possible) relative to the prevailing economic condition of scarcity.

G.22 _____. "Health Care and the United States Economic System." MILBANK MEMORIAL FUND QUARTERLY 50 (April 1972): 211-37.

A. C^S, P^S, PK

B. Major emphasis is here given to indicating the place of health care in the U.S. economic system and to showing how related economic concepts can contribute to an understanding of health care problems. Simplified definitions and health applications of the following economic concepts are provided: optimality, types of economic systems, the competitive market, deviations in the health field from the competitive market (including fewness of sellers, cooperation [collusion] among sellers, restrictions on entry, disequilibrium, and high information costs), and externalities. A closing integration with technology and technological change is also provided, stressing the fact that "the most pressing problems are not centered around technology and their solutions will probably be found in other directions. [Thus], we need to make health care markets work better; we need to quantify and control the exter-

nalities that affect health; and we need to recognize the importance of individual behavior and personal responsibility for
health. Substantial alterations in organization, financing
and education are required to achieve these objectives." This
is an effective nontechnical study interrelating economics and
the U.S. health care system.

G.23 _____. "Productivity in Services: Three Case Studies." In THE SER-
VICE ECONOMY, pp. 115-27. New York: National Bureau of Economic Research, 1968.

A. P^S

B. "Traditionally, output has been measured in terms of the
number of physician visits, or number of patient-days in a
hospital." Acknowledging the existence of conceptual and
statistical difficulties in the measurement and analysis of productivity, Fuchs suggests that: "This [traditional] approach is
roughly comparable to measuring the output of the automobile
industry in terms of the number of cars produced without regard
to size, durability, performance characteristics, and so on....
[This] provides only a crude approximation to the desired measure....The problem of measuring changes in the real output
of the medical care industry consists of three parts. First, the
various types of output must be defined; second, the changes
in each type must be quantified; and third, the various types
must be made commensurate, that is the changes must be translated into dollar equivalents." Fuchs notes in his summary:
"As some new work on demand theory stresses [see Becker, chapter 6, section C, and Grossman (G.28)], it is the individual (if
anyone) who produces health, using medical care as an input.
A reconciliation between this realistic view of medical care
and the conventional approaches to measuring output and productivity has not yet been achieved."

G.24 _____. "What Kind of System for Health Care?" BULLETIN OF THE
NEW YORK ACADEMY OF MEDICINE 45 (March 1969): 255-70.

A. C^S, P^S

B. In his introductory remarks, Fuchs examines "what we mean
by a system and why we need a system." He categorically
describes economic systems, citing, in particular, advantages
and disadvantages of the market system. Using the market
system as a base, he discusses the "medical care system" in
terms of deviations from the market system. Given these deviations, roles of the government are then suggested. To make
judgments about the best role for government, Fuchs classifies
the weaknesses of our present health care system into those of
ineffectiveness, inefficiency, and inequity. These correspond
roughly to the basic economic problems of what, how, and
for whom. In his conclusion, he suggests some general reme-

dies: First, reforms and changes are needed in medical practice
and medical education; second, hospitals should not be reimbursed on the basis of costs. "If ever there was a system
built to produce inefficiency, it is reimbursement according
to costs." Also, hospital systems must be developed to increase efficiency and effectiveness. Finally, four principles
of medical care financing are set forth.

G.25 _____. WHO SHALL LIVE? HEALTH, ECONOMICS, AND SOCIAL
CHOICE. New York: Basic Books, 1974. 168 p.

A. C^S, P^S

B. In general, the purpose of this book is to help "define the
problems, acquire the necessary facts, and understand the critical individual and social choices that must be made" in relation to the U.S. crisis in health care. Fuchs introduces his
book by identifying a set of integrated themes for subsequent
development in the remaining chapters: (1) the connection between health and medical care is not nearly as direct as most
discussions presume; genetic and environmental factors as well
as personal behavior are also very important; (2) the patient,
not the physician, has the major influence on his own health,
but the physician dominates with respect to medical care costs;
(3) given (2), the folly of trying to meet the problem of access by training more medical specialists and subspecialists is
discussed; (4) no magic payment formula exists that can transfer the cost of medical care from individuals to government or business; (5) choice must be available at both the
individual and social levels--a theme central to the entire
book.

G.26 Fuchs, V[ictor].R.; Rand, Elizabeth; and Garrett, Bonnie. "The Distribution
of Earnings in Health and Other Industries." In ESSAYS IN THE ECONOM-
ICS OF HEALTH AND MEDICAL CARE, edited by V.R. Fuchs, pp.
119-31. New York: National Bureau of Economic Research, 1972.

A. HK

B. The size distribution of earnings within industries "can provide insights concerning the distribution of human capital...
and the variation of these distributions across industries. In
addition, the analysis of intraindustry distributions may help
us to understand better certain problems in industrial organization and labor market behavior." Given this rationale, the
authors compared the distribution of earnings of full-time-year-
round employed persons in twenty large industries for the year
1959. "The health industry [was] found to have an extraordi-
nary bimodal distribution. Possible explanations for this marked
discontinuity are discussed and some questions for further research are raised."

C. Empirical

G.27 Ginzberg, Eli. "The Political Economy of Health." Paper presented to the Committee on Social Policy for Health Care, New York Academy of Medicine, held May 1968 in New York City, 1969.

A. C^S, P^S

B. This paper first provides some widely accepted formulations about the economics of health, including the demand for services, the supply of manpower, physician earnings, drug costs, and the costs of hospital care. In the context of these five areas, "significant imperfections prevail that severely limit and perhaps vitiate the application of theories derived from a model of the competitive market." Next, the following crucial problem areas are analyzed: financial constraints as a barrier to access, inadequacy of the existing insurance system, the inefficient and ineffective organization of our system, and the level of investment in health and medicine. Using his discussion of these problem areas, Ginzberg returns (in part II) to the formulations set forth initially and discusses them in the context of market controls (government and voluntary).

G.28 Grossman, Michael. THE DEMAND FOR HEALTH: A THEORETICAL AND EMPIRICAL INVESTIGATION. National Bureau of Economic Research Occasional Paper 119. New York: Columbia University Press, 1972. 115 p.

A. C^S

B. "The aims of this study are to construct and estimate a model of the demand for the commodity 'good health'." (The significance of this development is perceived as being twofold: "First, the level of ill health, measured by the rates of mortality and morbidity, influences the amount and productivity of labor supplied to an economy. Second,...what consumers demand when they purchase medical services [is] not these services per se but rather 'good health'.") "Given that the fundamental demand is for good health, it seems logical to study the demand for medical care by first constructing a model of the demand for health itself." This model, then, is based on a fundamental distinction between commodities and market goods. Here commodities are defined as fundamental objects of choice, produced by consumers with inputs of market goods and their own time. (For example, consumers use sporting equipment and their own time to produce the commodity recreation.) The commodity good health is treated as a durable item, health capital being one component of human capital. (This represents a unique study worthy of careful examination.)

C. Theoretical, quantitative methods

See also:

(1) Grossman, Michael. "On the Concept of Health Capital

and the Demand for Health." JOURNAL OF POLITICAL ECON-
OMY 80 (March/April 1972): 223-55.

(2) Newhouse, Joseph P., and Phelps, Charles E. "Price and
Income Elasticities for Medical Care Services." (entry 1.49)

(3) Becker, G.S. "A Theory of the Allocation of Time."
ECONOMIC JOURNAL 75 (September 1965): 493-517.

G.29 Hansen, W. Lee. "An Appraisal of Physician Manpower Projections."
INQUIRY 7 (March 1970): 102-13.

A. HK

B. "This paper focuses on three distinct but related topics.
The first concerns the objectives of physician manpower projections and several key questions which are raised about the
projections. The second reviews the empirical evidence on
the quality of physician manpower projections through an examination of the available projections for 1975 and 1965. And
the third section discusses some of the research that seems to
be needed to enlarge our understanding of the physician manpower market and hence to help improve physician projections."

G.30 _____. "'Shortages' and Investment in Health Manpower." In THE ECO-
NOMICS OF HEALTH AND MEDICAL CARE, Proceedings of a conference
held May 1962, Ann Arbor, Mich., edited by S.J. Axelrod, pp. 75-91.
Ann Arbor: University of Michigan Press, 1964.

A. HK

B. Hansen proposes to examine the basic evidence on which
physician and dentist shortages are predicted, and to set forth
several criteria by which the existence of shortages can be
judged in a meaningful economic sense. Rather than relying
upon changes in practitioner-population ratios or in relative
income positions, the author proposes "to make comparisons
between the rates of return which can be expected from investment in alternative types of professional training. The
proposed approach has the obvious advantage of considering
both the costs and returns of professional career choices." It
is found that rates of return to medical and dental education
can be estimated and that, in recent years, there has been a
rapid decrease in shortages. The paper contains (1) review
and critical analysis of the Bane Report; (2) discussion of
the "projective shortage" and relative income approaches
to determining shortages; (3) Hansen's rate-of-return approach; and (4) estimates based on the Hansen approach.

G.31 Harrison, Jeffrey L., and Nash, Kent D. "A New Approach to the Physician Shortage." INQUIRY 9 (March 1972): 34-39.

A. HK

B. "In this study [the authors] are concerned with the methods of financing the education of medical students and the effect on the supply of physicians. The first section discusses the asserted physician shortage as reported in various studies. The second section contains a brief description of the economic status of medical students enrolled in public and private institutions. The last section contains an analysis of full-cost tuition [with fully-funded financial aid], deferred payments, and their implications for increasing the supply of physicians." It is suggested that these two proposals--full-cost tuition, deferred payment--actually affect two aspects of the physician shortage problem. "First, by allocating financial subsidies on the basis of need or by allowing qualified medical students to defer tuition payments, the pool of qualified applicants is enlarged. Second,...funds presently committed to medical education but currently being used to subsidize students would be released for expansion of medical education facilities."

G.32 Hartwell, R.M. "The Economic History of Medical Care." In THE ECONOMICS OF HEALTH AND MEDICAL CARE, Proceedings of a conference held by the International Economic Association, April 1973, Tokyo, edited by Mark Perlman, pp. 3-20. New York: John Wiley and Sons, 1973.

A. HK

B. "The history of medical care divides into two periods, separated by the Industrial Revolution. If the history of mankind can be described as 'the history of poverty, dirt, and disease,' these three major obstacles to wealth, health and population growth have been overcome only in the advanced economies of the last two centuries. Nevertheless, the inheritance of the pre-industrial age was (a) a great deal of medical knowledge which was ineffective operationally and (b) ideas of social control (of doctors) and prevention (e.g., of leprosy, plague, etc.). The Industrial Revolution (including an agricultural revolution and, therefore, a nutritional revolution) was followed by a public health revolution (mid-nineteenth century) and a medical revolution (only in the twentieth century). For most of history, medical care has been irrelevant in the determination of aggregate social indices..."

G.33 Holtmann, A.G. "Prices, Time, and Technology in the Medical Care Market." JOURNAL OF HUMAN RESOURCES 7 (Spring 1972): 179-90.

A. c^S, p^S

B. The theoretical base for this paper is an article by Gary S. Becker ("A Theory of the Allocation of Time," ECONOMIC JOURNAL, September 1965), which revises the traditional theory of consumer behavior. Holtmann begins with a simple model of consumer behavior: He assumes "that the consumer is faced with a choice between two goods, that all income is used in consumption, that time is used in consumption, and that the consumer must use commodities in consuming a good." (See, in this context, the work by Michael Grossman, entry G.28). Following the model development section is a comparative statics analysis in which it is "shown that there are income and substitution effects that are substantially different from those associated with traditional theory....[Furthermore, it is] found that the value of the consumer's time, as well as the cost of the physician's time and medical commodities, is important in the medical services the consumer selects....[Thus]...the value of time should not be ignored. Indeed, the cost of time necessary to consume medical care is a major part of the cost."

C. Quantitative methods

G.34 Jeffers, James R.; Bognanno, Mario F.; and Bartlett, John C. "On the Demand Versus Need for Medical Services and the Concept of 'Shortage'." AMERICAN JOURNAL OF PUBLIC HEALTH 61 (January 1971): 46–63.

A. C^S

B. "The purposes of this article are to differentiate between the two concepts, 'need' and 'demand,' and to provide two interpretations of the concept of 'shortage' as it applies to medical services....[The] first section briefly discusses the concept of the 'need for medical services' [normative professional medical judgment]. This is followed by a section outlining the economist's notion of the 'demand for medical services.' The next section interrelates the two concepts. This is followed by a section interpreting the concept of shortage, and a final section presents a summary and the conclusions..." (provided in an excellent summary table).

G.35 Joseph, Hyman. "Empirical Research on the Demand for Health Care." INQUIRY 8 (March 1971): 61–71.

A. C^S

B. This is a two-part paper: "The first section analyzes the important determinants of the demand for health care: own price, prices of substitutes or complements, income and tastes. The measures of these determinants that are important to economists for policy purposes are described, and potential measurement difficulties are discussed. Section two critically reviews nine empirical studies of the demand for health care."

G.36 Klarman, Herbert E. "Economic Aspects of Projecting Requirements for Health Manpower." JOURNAL OF HUMAN RESOURCES 4 (Summer 1969): 360–76.

A. HK

B. Basically, Klarman provides here "a review, critique, and synthesis of, as well as [a] contribution to, the expanding [economic] literature on health manpower requirements..." As an introductory base, two other approaches to projecting manpower requirements are discussed--need as determined by professional standards, and personnel-to-population ratios. Klarman suggests that "the primary difference between the economist's and other approaches is that the former doubts the fixity of ratios among the several categories of health personnel or to a population, and asserts the technical possibility of substituting among health occupations..." Three principal economic approaches to projecting manpower requirements are then summarized--the population and income method, the method of constant utilization rates for a changed population, and the use of regression analysis to project expenditures for a particular type of service. "Part II of the paper deals with approaches to determining whether or not a shortage of personnel has existed." Included in this second section are these measurement devices: criterion ratio, position vacancies, relative earnings, and rate of return. "Part III of the paper extends the usual discussion of the requirements for manpower in two ways. It puts on the demand side of the equation items that generally occur under the heading of supply--gains in provider productivity and requirements for replacement."

G.37 Leveson, Irving. "Comments on Demand Analysis Papers." In EMPIRICAL STUDIES IN HEALTH ECONOMICS, edited by Herbert Klarman, pp. 165-67. Baltimore: Johns Hopkins Press, 1970.

A. C^S

B. This is a brief, well-formulated comment on the need for including the variable health in medical care demand analysis. It provides an important yet frequently ignored perspective to that analysis.

G.38 _____. "Medical Care Cost Incentives: Some Questions and Approaches for Research." INQUIRY 5 (December 1968): 3-13.

A. FK

B. At the outset, a clearer definition of the problem(s) of incentives in reimbursement mechanisms for medical care is attempted. The range of incentives in reimbursement alternatives is then examined, followed by research suggestions relating to types of incentive systems and specific reimbursement methods.

G.39 Lindsay, Cotton M. "Medical Care and the Economics of Sharing." ECONOMICA 36 (November 1969): 351-62.

A. C^S, P^S

B. "This paper provides an economic explanation of the observed widespread support of direct public provision of medical care. It is based on a characteristic of the relevant market different from characteristics which underlie various arguments in support of public provision....That aspect is the apparently universal desire and willingness to share. It is the attitude often expressed that everyone should have 'equal access' to the medical resources available....This argument runs throughout the literature of medical economics, but it has never to my [Lindsay's] knowledge been examined formally for its economic as opposed to its normative content. This paper attempts to fill this void."

C. Theoretical

See also:

Culyer, A.J. "Medical Care and the Economics of Giving." (entry G.14)

G.40 _____. "Real Returns to Medical Education." JOURNAL OF HUMAN RESOURCES 8 (Summer 1973): 331-48.

A. HK

B. "Conventional techniques for assessing the net returns on investment in training contain a bias positively associated with earnings and, hence, the level of investment required for a career....The bias results from an important measurement of the increased productivity of work associated with training.... As the training investment required for medical practice [is]... substantial, it is possible that the high returns reported [in the three studies] here may simply reflect this bias. In this paper [Lindsay reexamines] evidence of the high profitability of medicine, employing techniques which eliminate this bias....When this bias is eliminated, rents on medical training reported in these studies disappear. These findings fail to support the popular belief that the medical profession restrains entry by limiting medical school capacity. The paper suggests other ways in which the profession may be exploiting its monopoly power which go undetected in such profitability tests."

G.41 Mushkin, Selma J. "Health as an Investment." JOURNAL OF POLITICAL ECONOMY 70 (Supplement, 1962): 129-57.

A. HK

B. "A theory of human capital is in the process of formulation. The primary question is 'What is the contribution of changes in the quality of people to economic growth'?" Investment through education and health are two primary means to "improved quality." ("The concept of human capital formation through both education and health services rests on the twin notions that people as productive agents are improved by investment in these services and that the outlays made yield a continuing return in the future.") These two means (education and health) are briefly compared and contrasted in the introduction to this paper. The second part deals with capital formation through health care and returns to investment in health. Measures of capital formation through health programs are summarized and a central problem in assessing yields and investment in health is identified thereby for subsequent discussion-- i.e., the problem of the measurement of labor product added through health care. "The gain in (labor) resources through prevention or cure of disease and reduction in death, disability, and debility must, for the first stage of the estimate, be stated in terms of units of productive work time added. The second stage...is to assign a (dollar) value to these units." With respect to productive work time added, Mushkin concentrates on reduction in death rates. Because of limited data, gains from reduced disability and debility are not addressed. Regarding assignment of a dollar value, two approaches are set forth: (1) measurement of the costs of rearing a child, or of developing a productive labor force; and (2) a capital stock measure of the present value of future work that may be gained through eradication or control of disease.

G.42 Mushkin, Selma J., and Weisbrod, Burton A. "Investment in Health- Lifetime Health Expenditures on the 1960 Work Force." In THE ECONOM- ICS OF HEALTH AND MEDICAL CARE, Proceedings of a conference held May 1962, Ann Arbor, Mich., edited by S.J. Axelrod, pp. 257-70. Ann Arbor: University of Michigan Press, 1964.

A. C^S

B. "In this paper we shall attempt to take a small step in the direction of determining how much economic growth can be traced to investment in the health of our population. Specifically, we shall estimate the value of privately and public provided resources which have been devoted to the health of persons employed in 1960, over their lifetimes. We shall then see how the magnitude of these expenditures on health compares with the corresponding expenditures on schooling. We shall also compare the magnitude of health resources embodied in the 1960 work force and the resources in the 1960 stock of physical capital. In the process we shall note changes through time in the pattern of private health expenditures by age, and changes in the mix of private and public expenditures on health." Expenditures on the following health services are included in the analysis: physician services, hospital care, dental services, drugs, environmental health, medical research, and sanitation.

C. Empirical

G.43 Newhouse, Joseph P. "Does an Increase in the Price of a Necessity Re- duce Welfare More Than an Increase in the Price of a Luxury?" INQUIRY 9 (June 1972): 77-79.

A. P^SF

B. The basic question addressed in this note can be rephrased as follows: "If the government is to concern itself with particular price increases, is there more reason to be concerned about the price increase of a necessity?" In this context, Newhouse suggests: "The price increase that causes the greatest decrease in welfare is independent of which good is a 'necessity,' if necessity is given any usual meaning such as low marginal income elasticity or low price elasticity." Using this viewpoint as a basis for his discussion, the author concludes: "[There] may be a reason to be concerned about the behavior of medical care prices--but the reason is not that medical care is a 'necessity'."

See also:

(1) Ward, Richard A. "Does an Increase in the Price of a Necessity Reduce Welfare More Than an Increase in the Price of a Luxury? A Comment." INQUIRY 10 (March 1973): 64.

> Here, Ward argues with the Newhouse approach, stating that: "Because of the special nature of medical care, it is somewhat inappropriate to depict it on a preference map designed to represent utility scales. Medical care is a cost which must be subtracted from income--a lowering of the budget line --before utility maximization can begin....For most goods, the consumer can defend himself against welfare losses by substituting away from a good whose relative price rises. No such substitution is possible for medical care--a fact which does give cause for special attention to price behavior in this sector."

(2) Newhouse, Joseph P. "A Reply to Ward." INQUIRY 10 (June 1973): 73.

> Newhouse here replies that "there is overwhelming evidence against" the statements given in (1) above, concluding that "Ward's assertion and, thus, his comment are groundless."

G.44 Pauly, Mark V. MEDICAL CARE AT PUBLIC EXPENSE: A STUDY IN APPLIED WELFARE ECONOMICS. New York: Frederick A. Praeger, Publishers, 1971. 160 p.

A. C^S, FK

B. "This book explores the economic efficiency of public policy with respect to the provision of medical care at public expense." The main purpose is "to determine whether there are any general principles which can be set down that should govern the provision of medical care at public expense." Judgments about a system of public provision (i.e., through the use of tax funds) requires answers to two distinct sets of ques-

tions. The first set inquires about the rationale of public provision; thus, the first part of Pauly's study is concerned with
choosing a suitable criterion or rationale for public provision.
The second set examines the relationship between means and
ends. Given the determinants of a rationale, it becomes possible to describe the shape of an optimal system. "This 'model'
of an optimal system...[is] then...used to evaluate and compare methods, both current and proposed, for public provision
of medical care in the United States." Welfare economics is
used as the theoretical basis for this study. ("Welfare economics deals with the question of the efficiency or inefficiency
of various arrangements by evaluating them with the criterion
called 'Pareto optimality'.") Further, it should be noted that
"this study is specifically limited to consideration of public
provision," where this refers to the demand for health care.
Possible alterations in the way medical care is supplied or produced are not considered.

G.45 Perlman, Mark. "Economic History and Health Care in Industrialized Nations." In THE ECONOMICS OF HEALTH AND MEDICAL CARE, Proceedings of a conference held by the International Economic Association,
April 1973, Tokyo, edited by Mark Perlman, pp. 21-33. New York:
John Wiley and Sons, 1973.

A. C^S, P^S

B. "The focus is on three points: Medical care delivery is only
a subset of health protection systems. Indeed, from a historical standpoint, nutritional improvement, establishment of sani-
tary control and the spread of educational achievement in industrialized nations have been clearly more significant for im-
proving the health of nations (particularly in the reduction or
postponement of mortality) than medical delivery has been.
Second, our imperfect mortality data...must be supplemented
by a sophisticated collection of morbidity data....The design
for such data collection must basically be the responsibility
of epidemiologists and biostatisticians; only after they have
completed their tasks can the analytical contributions of economists ring true. Finally, the two methods upon which economists have relied, investment in human capital (essentially
an aspect of benefit-cost studies) and production function analysis (leading to an examination of substitutabilities), have in-
herent logical inadequacies. None the less [sic], the product
has served to improve our understanding of the problems....It
is reasonable to expect that these techniques, coupled with
better data and refined perceptions of the priority of problems,
will serve us even better in the future."

G.46 Reder, M.W. "Some Problems in the Measurement of Productivity in the
Medical Care Industry." In PRODUCTION AND PRODUCTIVITY IN THE
SERVICE INDUSTRIES, edited by Victor R. Fuchs, pp. 95-131. New

York: National Bureau of Economic Research, 1969.

A. P^S

B. This paper addresses some problems of conceptual specification as they relate to productivity measurement. In a discussion
following the paper, Herbert Klarman summarizes Reder's purpose
in this manner: "...Reder proposes that the following be done to
measure change in the productivity of medical care.

> 1. Express the change as the ratio of change in
> physical output over the change in deflated inputs.

> 2. Define output preferably as services available to
> a subscriber to a comprehensive health insurance
> plan. Alternatively, in more realistic circumstances,
> express output in terms of the number of episodes of
> illness treated.

> 3. Adjust the above ratio by taking account of
> changes in quality. Five measures of quality are
> variously suggested: life years gained, rates of un-
> detected illness, appropriateness of the process of
> diagnosis and treatment, patient satisfaction, and
> work days lost. Marginal rates of substitution
> (trade-offs) among the several measures of quality
> are to be obtained in a measure not specified."

See also:

(1) Klarman, Herbert E. "Discussion." PRODUCTION AND
PRODUCTIVITY, pp. 132-39.

(2) Feldstein, Martin S. "Discussion." PRODUCTION AND
PRODUCTIVITY, pp. 139-46.

(3) Fabricant, S., and Hirsch, W.Z. "Comments." PRODUC-
TION AND PRODUCTIVITY, pp. 146-47.

(4) Reder, M.W. "Reply." PRODUCTION AND PRODUCTIV-
ITY, pp. 148-53.

G.47 Roberts, Markley. "Trends in the Organization of Health Services: The
Private Sector." In THE ECONOMICS OF HEALTH AND MEDICAL CARE,
Proceedings of a conference held May 1962, Ann Arbor, Mich., edited
by S.J. Axelrod, pp. 23-41. Ann Arbor: University of Michigan Press, 1964.

A. P^S, HK, PK

B. Roberts separates the organizational aspect from problems of
financing, deeming this separation as useful "in order to analyze how changes in the structure of health services affect
costs, prices, and financing of health services." His concern
for health services organization is further based on (1) a
rapidly rising demand for health services, and (2) rapid progress
in medical science and medical technology. Five trends in

the organization of health services are identified for subsequent discussion: (1) expansion of auxiliary health professions; (2) rising productivity of health personnel; (3) more rational organization of health facilities and services; (4) continuing experimentation in providing a framework for comprehensive health care; and (5) development of more effective controls applied to the costs, quantity, and quality of health services.

G.48 Robertson, Robert L. "Issues in Measuring the Economic Effects of Personal Health Services." MEDICAL CARE 5 (November/December 1967): 362-68.

A. C^S

B. "This paper is based upon a project...designed to measure effects of personal health services, particularly work time saved and resulting earnings." The following conceptual and methodological issues relating to this project are here discussed: input measurement and complementarities (joint uses) among medical inputs, the consumption/investment aspects of health care inputs, output identification and measurement plus functional connection to inputs, the "multiple disease problem," and sample bias.

G.49 Sgontz, Larry G. "The Economics of Financing Medical Care: A Review of the Literature." INQUIRY 9 (December 1972): 3-19.

A. FK

B. This article deals with the economic aspects of alternative financing systems and mechanisms and covers the following topics: "the classification of financing systems; the relative importance of alternative financing systems in the United States; situations that may call for the public financing of medical care; and a general analysis of some existing and proposed measures for public provision of medical care."

G.50 Silver, Morris. "An Econometric Analysis of Spatial Variations in Mortality Rates by Race and Sex." In ESSAYS IN THE ECONOMICS OF HEALTH AND MEDICAL CARE, edited by V.R. Fuchs, pp. 161-227. New York: National Bureau of Economic Research, 1972.

A. C^S

B. "The wish to measure the effects of income, schooling, and a variety of other variables upon mortality and to isolate their [roles] in explaining the difference in mortality rates of whites and blacks in the United States is the primary factor motivating this study. To accomplish this...multiple regression analysis [is applied] to 1959-61 age-adjusted mortality rates by race and sex for states and standard metropolitan statistical areas (SMSA's)....A major objective...is to cast additional light on the relationship between income and mortality. In particular, an effort [is] made to determine whether the relationship across SMSA's is different from that across states, how the income effect varies with sex and race, what the influence of the multicollinearity between income and schooling consists in, and whether the source of income (labor or nonlabor) is relevant."

C. Empirical, quantitative methods

G.51 _____. "An Economic Analysis of Variations in Medical Expenses and Work-Loss Rates." In ESSAYS IN THE ECONOMICS OF HEALTH AND MEDICAL CARE, edited by V.R. Fuchs, pp. 97-118. New York: National Bureau of Economic Research, 1972.

A. C^S

B. "This paper employs a number of the standard tools of economic analysis to explore unpublished data on the medical expenses and work-loss days due to injury of currently employed persons." Medical expense data (1961-62) and work-loss data (1962-63) were drawn from the National Health Survey of the National Center for Health Statistics. Using income measures and sex/age groupings by region of the country, six dependent variables are examined--total medical expense (subdivided by hospital, medicine, doctor, and dentist expenses) and work-loss days. Income elasticities are generated for the demand for medical care, and the validity of using the work-loss rate as a measure of health is tested by "ascertaining whether variations in work-loss rates reflect differences in the degree to which individuals can afford to lose income or in the amounts that would be lost, and if so, the extent to which they do so."

C. Empirical, quantitative methods

G.52 Stewart, Charles T., Jr. "Allocation of Resources to Health." JOURNAL OF HUMAN RESOURCES 6 (Winter 1971): 103-22.

A. P^S

B. "This article suggests a classification of activities whose primary objective is the improvement and/or preservation of health." This classification--treatment, prevention, information, and research--"aims to facilitate rational decision-making in the health area by grouping alternative means to the same objective and organizing systems and subsystems in a functional hierarchy and sequence. A preliminary attempt is made to judge the nature of tradeoffs and interactions between systems at a given point in time in order to allocate resources among them. Some suggestions are also made on proper sequencing and, therefore, allocation of resources among systems over time." The author contends that: "The typical relation between treatment and prevention is competitive, whereas that between information and research is complementary, as is the relation between the two pairs of subsystems. The four subsystems also differ in scale effects and in their temporal and spatial characteristics, affecting allocative choice between them....An illustrative test of productivity is made in order to evaluate present allocation and guide improved allocation in the future....Using life expectancy as the dependent variable, an attempt was made to measure the significance of treatment variables, literacy (proxy for information), and potable water (proxy for prevention) for all nations in the Western Hemisphere. Both literacy and potable water proved highly significant, whereas none of the treatment variables are significantly related to life expectancy. Data from the United States also suggest a low marginal productivity of medical treatment in terms of life expectancy. Alternative explanations are discussed, together with indicated reallocation of resources away from medical treatment."

See also:

Meeker, Edward. "Allocation of Resources to Health Revisited." JOURNAL OF HUMAN RESOURCES 8 (Spring 1973): 257-59.

> "In this paper [Meeker demonstrates] that Stewart's econometric results suffer from specification error; had he specified his model correctly, his regression results would have been significantly different. [He also shows] that his [Stewart's] method of analyzing the productivity of improvements in medicine in the United States makes it virtually impossible to reject the hypothesis that medical practice has a marginal productivity near zero. Finally, [Meeker points] out that [Stewart's] economic analysis is methodologically incorrect."

G.53 Weisbrod, Burton A. "Collective-Consumption Services of Individual-Consumption Goods." QUARTERLY JOURNAL OF ECONOMICS 78 (August 1964): 471-77.

A. C^S, P^S

B. "The principal objectives of this paper are: (1) to point out that a number of significant commodities exist which apparently are of an individual-consumption variety, but which also possess characteristics of a pure collective-consumption good; and (2) to discuss some implications of this observation, in particular showing that even if some apparently individual-consumption goods cannot profitably be provided by private enterprise it may serve the social welfare to subsidize their production." Weisbrod's development of the "option demand" concept is not here related primarily to the health care field, though suggestions concerning its applicability to hospitals are made. Furthermore, the concept has been subsequently applied (explicitly and implicitly) by other health economists.

See also:

(1) Long, Millard F. "Collective-Consumption Services of Individual-Consumption Goods: Comment." QUARTERLY JOURNAL OF ECONOMICS 81 (May 1967): 351-52.

(2) Lindsay, Cotton M. "Option Demand and Consumer's Surplus." QUARTERLY JOURNAL OF ECONOMICS 83 (May 1969): 344-46.

(3) Byerlee, D.R. "Option Demand and Consumer Surplus: Comment." QUARTERLY JOURNAL OF ECONOMICS 85 (August 1971): 523-27.

(4) Cicchetti, Charles J., and Freeman, A. Myrick III. "Option Demand and Consumer Surplus: Further Comment." QUARTERLY JOURNAL OF ECONOMICS 85 (August 1971): 528-39.

G.54 Whipple, David. "Health Care as a Right: Its Economic Implications." INQUIRY 11 (March 1974): 65-68.

A. FK

B. Given the growing predominance of the "adequate health care is a right" attitude, Whipple's purpose is mainly to examine the financial structure implications that derive from that attitude. A conceptual consideration of adequate health care is followed by an examination of government's role, and it is suggested that "except for relatively small user charges for certain kinds of services, the government must somehow (as they do in education) disassociate charges from access." A "Voucher Plan" is proposed which would entitle an individual "to purchase a plan providing basic health care services and catastrophic coverage. Its value would be independent of income, although not with respect to the mode of provision [prepayment or fee-for-service]. There would exist two (usually) distinct redemption values for the voucher, depending on who redeems the voucher."

G.55 Wirick, Grover, and Barlow, Robin. "The Economic and Social Determinants of the Demand for Health Services." In THE ECONOMICS OF HEALTH AND MEDICAL CARE, Proceedings of a conference held May 1962, Ann Arbor, Mich., edited by S.J. Axelrod, pp. 95-125. Ann Arbor: University of Michigan Press, 1964.

A. C^S

B. "The first part of this discussion is largely concerned with the nature of the preference function for medical care, after which a theoretical model of the demand for medical care is developed and compared with models used in other studies. A

new application of statistical methodology is described having
special advantages for this type of analysis, and coefficients
are estimated from data collected in a survey of Michigan families." The authors include the following variables as bases for the
demand for health care: existence of real physiological needs;
perception of real or supposed needs; willingness to meet felt
needs by securing medical care; and ability to secure medical
care. Ultimately, a multivariate method, basically an analysis
of variance technique, is used to determine the impact on
demand of eight variables--physiological needs (age, sex),
willingness to secure care (attitudes toward early care, education, and region where head of family grew up), and ability
to secure care (family income, number of equivalent adults,
health insurance coverage).

C. Quantitative methods, empirical

See also:

Fuchs, Victor R. "Comment." ECONOMICS OF HEALTH,
pp. 125-27.

G.56 Yett, Donald E. "The Chronic 'Shortage' of Nurses: A Public Policy
Dilemma." In EMPIRICAL STUDIES IN HEALTH ECONOMICS, edited by
Herbert Klarman, pp. 357-89. Baltimore: Johns Hopkins Press, 1970.

A. HK

B. This empirical analysis of the supply of nursing labor employs both historical and theoretical bases. Furthermore, there
are both implicit and explicit examinations of the policy implications with respect to shortages of nurses. (See "Comment"
by Sherwin Rosen and "Rejoinder" by Donald Yett. EMPIRI-
CAL STUDIES, pp. 390-97.)

C. Theoretical, empirical, quantitative methods

B. MISCELLANEOUS - "MINOR" SUBJECT AREAS

_.57 Bailey, Richard M. "Economics and Planning." In NOTES ON COMPRE-
HENSIVE PLANNING FOR HEALTH, edited by Henrik L. Blum and As-
sociates, pp. 9.01-9.45. Berkeley: Comprehensive Health Planning
Unit, School of Public Health, University of California, 1968.

A. C^S, P^S

B. Basically, the concern of this chapter is public sector medicine in the context of the developing orientation labeled "comprehensive health planning." Government "is increasingly
withdrawing from the production of medical services and focusing upon a new role, that of being a large collective consumer
interested in advancing the interests of those patients whose
care and treatment is being paid for by the government. In

this new role, government is concerned with obtaining maximum effectiveness from the purchases of medical services... [i.e.]...to achieve an optimal return on its investment for society as a whole." Thus, Bailey here emphasizes that: "By taking a leadership position, raising questions about inadequacies and directing funds into new efforts, the government can fulfill a function which the 'unseen hand' of the market is not capable of achieving. [He notes, however, that] the government actions cannot succeed without relying upon the multitude of private decisions by all participants in the health care system. Therefore, unless it wishes to take over and operate the industry, government must realize that it must usually work through, not against, the present system for producing and distributing health care." The concerns are, in summary, the evolution of national economic policy and the claims that health expenditures make upon national resources.

_.58 Bailey, Richard M., and Tierney, Thomas M., Jr. "Costs, Service Differences, and Prices in Private Clinical Laboratories." HEALTH AND SOCIETY (formerly MILBANK MEMORIAL FUND QUARTERLY) 52 (Summer 1974): 265-89.

A. $P^S PK$, F

B. "The factors that have led to the increased importance of laboratory testing in the provision of health care services have caused radical changes in the clinical laboratory industry. The first in a series studying the economics of the industry, this article offers an examination of the varied structure of the industry and presents preliminary data on direct and indirect costs and prices. The paper focuses on the service component of the laboratory product, showing how service differences have influenced the structure of the industry and how they affect both the cost and price of laboratory tests." Furthermore, this initial effort concentrates "largely on the supply side of the activities of private clinical laboratories." The corporate growth of clinical laboratories is first set forth, followed by an examination of costs (direct and indirect), the laboratory product (or test), ancillary services, and laboratory prices. Their analysis is then applied to five laboratories of different sizes. They suggest that the direct production cost of a test may be quite small in relation to the indirect service costs and that, among the five sample laboratories, much of the price differential may be based on the number of ancillary services offered.

C. Empirical

_.59 Carr, W. John. "Economic Efficiency in the Allocation of Hospital Resources: Central Planning vs. Evolutionary Development." In EMPIRICAL STUDIES IN HEALTH ECONOMICS, edited by Herbert Klarman, pp. 195-221. Baltimore: Johns Hopkins Press, 1970.

A. C^S, P^S

B. Two basic types of economic models are constructed, one of a completely centralized planning system and the other of a pure market system. The intent is to compare the efficiency attainable under both market and planning resource allocation methods. (See "Comment" by Jerome Rothenberg, EMPIRICAL STUDIES, pp. 222-28.)

C. Empirical, quantitative methods

_.60 Doherty, Neville. "Excess Profits in the Drug Industry and Their Effect on Consumer Expenditures." INQUIRY 10 (September 1973): 19-30.

A. C^S, FK

B. "The primary objective is to measure the relationship that exists between high profits and drug expenditures. It is assumed that drug firms attempt to maximize profits and that rates of return on stockholders' equity are valid measures of a firm's or industry's earning power....Economic theories regarding profit are related to the high profits in the drug industry and these profits' bearing on drug expenditures are examined." The author derives "measures of foregone consumer purchasing power attributed to the exercise of monopoly power by the pharmaceutical manufacturers....Excess profits were calculated to cost the average family approximately $2.62 in 1971. On a national basis, overspending is exceeding $130 million per year. This can be looked at as the annual welfare loss attributable to the exercise of pure monopoly power..."

C. Empirical

_.61 Fein, R[ashi]. ECONOMICS OF MENTAL ILLNESS. Monograph Series no. 2. A Report to the Joint Commission on Mental Illness and Health. New York: Basic Books, 1958. 164 p.

A. HK

B. This study provides sound methods for computing the costs (direct and indirect) of mental illness. Basically, its concern is the development of reliable and meaningful cost figures as an aid to measuring both the extent of the mental illness problem and progress toward its solution.

_.62 Feldstein, Martin S. "An Aggregate Planning Model of the Health Care Sector." MEDICAL CARE 5 (November/December 1967): 369-81.

A. C^S, P^S

B. "A prerequisite of appropriate government policy is an understanding of the aggregate behavioral relations of the millions of independent producers and consumers whose decisions determine the supply and use of health care services. The purpose of this paper is to show how this information could be estimated and analyzed in the framework of an econometric model of [part of] the health care sector." Estimated behavioral relations are used to predict the impact of government "health action" on the pattern of availability and use of health care services. Two types of information are used in the development of this "conditional prediction planning" model-- monitoring information and explanatory information. The model is not one of the entire health sector; rather, it provides "a preliminary core for a larger model and permits exploring a problem of substantial importance, the supply [of] and demand for hospital inpatient care."

C. Theoretical, quantitative methods

_.63 _____. ECONOMIC ANALYSIS FOR HEALTH SERVICE EFFICIENCY. Chicago: Markham Publishing Co., 1968. 325 p.

For annotation see 6.3.

_.64 _____. "Health Sector Planning in Developing Countries." ECONOMI-CA 37 (May 1970): 139-63.

A. HK, PK, FK

B. "The current paper reports the first step towards the development of a systematic approach to health sector planning capable of integration into a more general programme of economic development. The aim of the present research has been to devise a potentially operational method for allocating the scarce health sector funds, manpower and facilities among different disease control programmes and individual activities in the way which yields the optimum feasible reduction of mortality, morbidity and economic losses. At the core of this method is a linear activity analysis description of the health care sector: a vector of inputs and a vector of outputs is associated with each health activity. This leads to an optimization procedure using a linear programming algorithm....Section I describes how the general health sector planning problem can be put into the form of a linear programming calculation. This is then illustrated by an application to planning within the tuberculosis control division. Section II specifies the model for this application and discusses the general problems of benefit measurement. Section III describes the characteristics of the optimal sets of activities obtained with different objective functions, considers the implications of the computed shadow prices, presents results to show the effects of larger changes in resource constraints, and compares the results of the analysis with the choices that would have been made by piecemeal cost-benefit analysis."

C. Quantitative methods

_.65 Ingbar, Mary Lee, with Lee, Sidney S. "Economic Analysis as a Tool of Program Evaluation: Costs in a Home Care Program." In THE ECONOMICS OF HEALTH AND MEDICAL CARE, Proceedings of a conference held May 1962, Ann Arbor, Mich., edited by S.J. Axelrod, pp. 173-210. Ann Arbor: University of Michigan Press, 1964.

For annotation see 1.25.

_.66 Leveson, Irving. "Access to Medical Care: The Queensbridge Experiment." INQUIRY 9 (June 1972): 61-68.

A. C^S

B. In a conceptual context, Leveson had set forth previously the postulate that as services are increasingly paid for by third parties, the roles of information and non-money "price" variables (e.g., consumer's time and travel) grow in importance. This paper considers the success of a particular effort to provide an entry point into the system. Using the Queensbridge Health Maintenance System--established to provide services without charge to the 1,400 residents aged sixty or over of the Queensbridge Housing Project, Long Island City--Leveson analyzes the determinants of whether persons even registered for this service program. Particular attention is paid to the role of health status in the demand for medical care, to separating the effects of income and education in disaggregated data, and to non-money "price" and information variables. Health status, income and education, and non-money "price" information variables were all found to have significant impact on demand, but the "most discouraging finding is the relatively low utilization rate of persons lacking an alternative usual source of care. Taken together with the relatively low utilization of the population as a whole, the data suggest that patients will not easily be attracted by an efficient entry point to the same unsatisfactory services as always."

_.67 Leifmann-Keil, Elisabeth. "Consumer Protection, Incentives and Externalities in the Drug Market." In THE ECONOMICS OF HEALTH AND MEDICAL CARE, Proceedings of a conference held by the International Economic Association, April 1973, Tokyo, edited by Mark Perlman, pp. 117-29. New York: John Wiley and Sons, 1973.

A. C^S, P^S

B. "The purpose of this paper is to analyze the influence of the requirements of prescription for ethical drugs on the position of the different participants in the drug market (D.M.) The consequences, intended and expected, of enforcing regulation to protect the ignorant consumer, namely prescription requirements for a growing share of drugs, are--as the paper demonstrates--not achieved....When examined, the protection of the consumer proves to be, first of all, not a protection of the demand (the consumer or patient) but a special legal frame-

work for protecting the physician and the pharmaceutical industry. The incentives for the physician and the pharmaceutical
industry to monopolize information and knowledge in respect to
ethical drugs are strengthened. The additional introduction of
a social sickness insurance scheme or a national health service
turns out to fortify the monopolistic positions of the physician
and the pharmaceutical industry. The position of the consumer
is thus further weakened. The guarantees of quality and safety
are imperfect, the economic interests of the consumer disre-
garded. The intention to achieve a reduction in social costs
results in additional social costs."

See also:

"Summary Record of Discussion." ECONOMICS OF HEALTH,
pp. 134-38.

_.68 McCaffree, Kenneth M. "The Economic Basis for the Development of
Community Mental Health Programs." MEDICAL CARE 6 (July/August
1968): 286-99.

For annotation see 5.2.

C. MISCELLANEOUS - NON-SYSTEMATIZED

Becker, G.S. "A Theory of the Allocation of Time." ECONOMIC JOURNAL
75 (September 1965): 493-517.

B. "The first section [of this paper] sets out a basic theoretical
analysis of choice that includes the cost of time on the same foot-
ing as the cost of market goods, while the remaining sections treat
various empirical implications of the theory. These include a new
approach to changes in hours of work and 'leisure,' the full integration of so-called 'productive' consumption into economic analysis, a new analysis of the effect of income on the quantity and
'quality' of commodities consumed, some suggestions on the measurement of productivity, an economic analysis of queues and a few
others as well." Becker summarizes his paper as follows: "At the
heart of the theory [of the allocation of time between different
activities] is an assumption that households are producers as well
as consumers; they produce commodities by combining inputs of
goods and time according to the cost-minimization rules of the
traditional theory of the firm. Commodities are produced in quantities determined by maximising [sic] a utility function of the commodity set subject to prices and a constraint on resources. Resources are measured by what is called full income, which is the
sum of money income and that foregone or 'lost' by the use of time
and goods to obtain utility, while commodity prices are measured
by the sum of the costs of their goods and time inputs. The effect of changes in earnings, other income, goods prices and the
productivity of working and consumption time on the allocation of

time and the commodity set has been analysed." Although this
article makes no reference to health or medical care, its relevance is demonstrated by Grossman in the study cited below.

C. Theoretical, quantitative methods

See also:

Grossman, Michael. THE DEMAND FOR HEALTH: A THEORETI-
CAL AND EMPIRICAL INVESTIGATION. (entry G.28)

Ginzberg, Eli. MEN, MONEY, AND MEDICINE. New York: Columbia University Press, 1969. 291 p.

B. This collection of essays is divided into four parts. "In Part
One, two themes predominate: What are reasonable expectations of a system of medical care for an affluent country which
still confronts many unmet needs? And what have been some of
the financial and manpower transformations of the system as the
nation has attempted to improve both the provision and distribution
of health services? In Part Two, the focus is on the critical role
of the physician...who stands at the apex of the system..." The
significance of their freedom to determine where and how they work
is emphasized. "Part Three is concerned with the ever-larger role
played by allied health manpower....Particular note is taken of
the potentialities and, even more, the limitations of the leadership
of specific occupational groups in rationalizing their training systems and altering employment practices so that their members can
work more effectively and receive higher compensation. Part Four
is concerned with illuminating the problems of persons suffering
from chronic conditions and the extent to which their medical needs
are intertwined with the socioeconomic structures in which they
work and live."

Hauser, M.M., ed. THE ECONOMICS OF MEDICAL CARE. London: George
Allen and Unwin, 1972. 334 p.

B. This book is a collection of readings demonstrating the relevance
and application of economic analysis to the field of medical care.
The variable condition of resource allocation represents the focus
of concern, a matter central to the discipline of economics and to
the reality of medical care provision. Topics included in this
text are: (1) efficiency and equality in medical care provision;
(2) economic analysis as a means of program assessment; (3) efficiency and planning in hospital care; (4) social accounting and
operational research in medical care; and (5) international studies.

Kelman, Sander. "Toward the Political Economy of Medical Care." INQUIRY
8 (September 1971): 30-38.

B. Dr. Kelman simply attempts "to make the case for a political
economic analysis of the American medical care system that is at
once historical in approach and critical in analysis. It provides

merely a skeleton of what would constitute a thorough political economic analysis." Specifically, an attempt is made to: "(1) Illustrate how the dynamics of the larger economic system are mirrored in the medical care system; (2) Raise the general issue of whether innovations in the medical care system that violate the premises of the larger system can ever be politically viable; and (3) Forecast the likely outcome of the current structural deliberations on the medical care system (national health insurance and health maintenance organizations) in terms of current developments in the banking and financial sector of the American economy."

Klarman, Herbert E. THE ECONOMICS OF HEALTH. New York: Columbia University Press, 1965. 200 p.

B. This excellent introductory text includes: (1) an overview of the health and medical care industry, with emphasis on the "economics of health"; (2) elements of supply and demand--factors influencing demand, supply of personnel and hospital services; and (3) organization, coordination, and regulation within the industry. A selected bibliography is appended.

Krause, Elliott A. "Health and the Politics of Technology." INQUIRY 8 (September 1971): 51-59.

B. Discussion here focuses on the broad political meanings of technological development in the health field--i.e., innovations and issues which the onset of technological medicine brings about. Reference is first made to Karl Marx and Auguste Comte, both of whom had theories concerning the role of industrial technology in bringing about a new social order. Since the use of technology in health is inherently a political as well as a scientific issue-- it involves the interests of people and groups of all types--the major "interested parties" are here briefly examined. Specifically, attention is focused on what these "parties" want and the social processes which determine whether they will get what they want.

Mushkin, Selma J. "Toward a Definition of Health Economics." PUBLIC HEALTH REPORTS 73 (September 1958): 785-93.

B. Mushkin's premise is that health economics "is concerned with the optimum use of scarce economic resources for the care of the sick and the promotion of health, taking into account competing uses of these resources. The basic problems are of two kinds: the organization of the medical market, and the net yield of investment in people for health."

_____. "Why Health Economics." In THE ECONOMICS OF HEALTH AND MEDICAL CARE, Proceedings of a conference held May 1962, Ann Arbor, Mich., edited by S.J. Axelrod, pp. 3-13. Ann Arbor: University of Michigan Press, 1964.

B. Some primary bases are set forth regarding the development of
health economics as a discipline. First, it is suggested that a
true understanding of the sources of economic growth requires "that
efforts be made to explore the economics of health, and the ways
in which the improved health of the people contributes to enlarg-
ing the resources and output of an economy." Second, in the context of public expenditure theory, the economist's "tools of input-
output analysis, of cost-benefit evaluations, of community development studies, for example, provide additional devices for the policy maker and additional guides to national decisions on health resource allocation." Third, an increasing share of national resources
is being devoted to health care. In summary, Mushkin states: "Essentially, however, it is the pressure for guides to policy formation,
the urgent demands for workable solutions to current problems that
compel the application of the tools of the economist to the problems of health care....The basic aid that the economist can offer
is to define the various possible courses of action and the consequences of the several choices."

Somers, Herman M., and Somers, Anne R. A PROGRAM FOR RESEARCH IN
HEALTH ECONOMICS. Health Economics Series no. 7. U.S. Department of
Health, Education, and Welfare--Public Health Service Publication no. 947-7.
Washington, D.C.: Government Printing Office, 1967. 43 p.

B. "This report contains the background paper for a conference of
experts on the economics of health care and medical research con-
vened by the Brookings Institution on October 29, 1965, together
with a summary of the conference discussion....The paper attempts
to focus upon public policy issues. It, therefore, takes a broad
view of 'health economics,' often including problems and questions
which go beyond the traditional boundaries of...economics."

Appendix A

AUTHORS AND TITLES OF TEXT ENTRIES

1.1 Ackroyd, Ted J. "Spatial Interaction Vectors: A Method for Examining the Spatial Distribution of Services among Non-Federal, Short-Term, General Hospitals." Doctoral dissertation, University of Iowa, 1974. 92 p.

G.1 Altman, Stuart H. "The Structure of Nursing Education and Its Impact on Supply." In EMPIRICAL STUDIES IN HEALTH ECONOMICS, edited by Herbert Klarman, pp. 335-52. Baltimore: Johns Hopkins Press, 1970.

G.2 Andersen, Ronald, and Anderson, Odin. A DECADE OF HEALTH SERVICES. Chicago: University of Chicago Press, 1967. 244 p.

G.3 Andersen, Ronald, and Benham, Lee. "Factors Affecting the Relationship between Family Income and Medical Care Consumption." In EMPIRICAL STUDIES IN HEALTH ECONOMICS, edited by Herbert Klarman, pp. 73-95. Baltimore: Johns Hopkins Press, 1970.

G.4 Arrow, Kenneth J. "Uncertainty and the Welfare Economics of Medical Care." AMERICAN ECONOMIC REVIEW 53 (December 1963): 941-73.

G.5 Auster, Richard; Leveson, Irving; and Sarachek, Deborah. "The Production of Health, an Exploratory Study." In ESSAYS IN THE ECONOMICS OF HEALTH AND MEDICAL CARE, edited by V.R. Fuchs, pp. 135-58. New York: National Bureau of Economic Research, 1972.

*_.57 Bailey, Richard M. "Economics and Planning." In NOTES ON COMPREHENSIVE PLANNING FOR HEALTH, edited by Henrik L. Blum and Associates, pp. 9.01-9.45. Berkeley: Comprehensive Health Planning Unit, School of Public Health, University of California, 1968.

2.1 _____. "Economies of Scale in Medical Practice." In EMPIRICAL STUDIES IN HEALTH ECONOMICS, edited by Herbert Klarman, pp. 255-73. Baltimore: Johns Hopkins Press, 1970.

For those items identified in multiple locations, an asterisk(*) is used to denote where the annotation is included.

G.6 _____ . "An Economist's View of the Health Services Industry." IN-QUIRY 6 (March 1969): 3-18.

2.2 _____ . "Philosophy, Faith, Fact and Fiction in the Production of Medical Services." INQUIRY 7 (March 1970): 37-53.

_.58 Bailey, Richard M., and Tierney, Thomas M., Jr. "Costs, Service Differences, and Prices in Private Clinical Laboratories." HEALTH AND SOCIETY (formerly MILBANK MEMORIAL FUND QUARTERLY) 52 (Summer 1974): 265-89.

3.1 Baird, Charles W. "A Proposal for Financing the Purchase of Health Services." JOURNAL OF HUMAN RESOURCES 5 (Winter 1970): 89-105.

1.2 Baron, David P. "A Study of Hospital Cost Inflation." JOURNAL OF HUMAN RESOURCES 9 (Winter 1974): 33-49.

G.7 Barzel, Yoram. "Productivity and the Price of Medical Services." JOURNAL OF POLITICAL ECONOMY 77 (November/December 1969): 1014-27.

M Becker, G.S. "A Theory of the Allocation of Time." ECONOMIC JOURNAL 75 (September 1965): 493-517.

G.8 Benham, Lee. "The Labor Market for Registered Nurses: A Three-Equation Model." REVIEW OF ECONOMICS AND STATISTICS 53 (August 1971): 246-52.

2.3 Benham, L[ee].; Maurizi, A.; and Reder, M.[W.]. "Migration, Location and Remuneration of Medical Personnel: Physicians and Dentists." REVIEW OF ECONOMICS AND STATISTICS 50 (August 1968): 332-47.

1.3 Berki, Sylvester E. HOSPITAL ECONOMICS. Lexington, Mass.: D.C. Heath and Co., 1972. 270 p.

G.9 Berkowitz, Monroe, and Johnson, William G. "Health and Labor Force Participation." JOURNAL OF HUMAN RESOURCES 9 (Winter 1974): 117-28.

1.4 Berry, Ralph E., Jr. "Cost and Efficiency in the Production of Hospital Services." HEALTH AND SOCIETY (formerly MILBANK MEMORIAL FUND QUARTERLY) 52 (Summer 1974): 291-313.

1.5 _____ . "On Grouping Hospitals for Economic Analysis." INQUIRY 10 (December 1973): 5-12.

1.6 _____. "Product Heterogeniety and Hospital Cost Analysis." INQUIRY 7 (March 1970): 67-75.

G.10 Bognanno, M[ario].F.; Hixson, J.S.; and Jeffers, J[ames].R. "The Short-Run Supply of Nurse's Time." JOURNAL OF HUMAN RESOURCES 9 (Winter 1974): 80-94.

G.11 Bognanno, Mario F., and Jeffers, James R. "Evidence on the Physician Shortage." Bureau of Business and Economic Research, College of Business Administration. Working Paper Series no. 71-13. Iowa City: University of Iowa, June 1971. 39 p.

G.12 Boulding, Kenneth. "The Concept of Need for Health Services." MILBANK MEMORIAL FUND QUARTERLY 44 (October 1966): 202-28.

1.7 Brinker, Paul A., and Walker, Burley. "The Hill-Burton Act: 1948-1954." REVIEW OF ECONOMICS AND STATISTICS 44 (May 1962): 208-12.

*_.59 Carr, W. John. "Economic Efficiency in the Allocation of Hospital Resources: Central Planning vs. Evolutionary Development." In EMPIRICAL STUDIES IN HEALTH ECONOMICS, edited by Herbert Klarman, pp. 195-221. Baltimore: Johns Hopkins Press, 1970.

1.9 Carr, W. John, and Feldstein, Paul J. "The Relationship of Cost to Hospital Size." INQUIRY 4 (June 1967): 45-65.

1.10 Cohen, Harold A. "Hospital Cost Curves with Emphasis on Measuring Patient Care Output." In EMPIRICAL STUDIES IN HEALTH ECONOMICS, edited by Herbert Klarman, pp. 279-93. Baltimore: Johns Hopkins Press, 1970.

1.11 _____. "Variations in Cost among Hospitals of Different Sizes." SOUTHERN ECONOMICS JOURNAL 33 (January 1967): 355-66.

1.12 Collins, Gavin L. "Cost Analysis and Efficiency Measures for Hospitals." INQUIRY 5 (June 1968): 50-61.

*6.1 Cooper, Michael. "Economics of Need: The Experience of the British Health Service." In THE ECONOMICS OF HEALTH AND MEDICAL CARE, Proceedings of a conference held by the International Economic Association, April 1973, Tokyo, edited by Mark Perlman, pp. 89-107. New York: John Wiley and Sons, 1973.

G.13 Culyer, A.J. "Is Medical Care Different? In HEALTH ECONOMICS, SELECTED READINGS, edited by M.H. Cooper and A.J. Culyer, pp.

49-74. Baltimore: Penguin Books, 1973.

*G.14 ____ . "Medical Care and the Economics of Giving." ECONOMICA 38 (August 1971): 295-303.

1.13 Davis, Karen. "Relationship of Hospital Prices to Costs." APPLIED ECONOMICS 3 (June 1971): 115-25.

1.14 ____ . "Theories of Hospital Inflation: Some Empirical Evidence." JOURNAL OF HUMAN RESOURCES 8 (Spring 1973): 181-201.

1.15 Davis, Karen, and Russell, Louise B. "The Substitution of Hospital Outpatient Care for Inpatient Care." REVIEW OF ECONOMICS AND STATISTICS 54 (May 1972): 109-20.

_.60 Doherty, Neville. "Excess Profits in the Drug Industry and Their Effect on Consumer Expenditures." INQUIRY 10 (September 1973): 19-30.

1.16 Ehrenberg, Ronald G. "Organizational Control and the Economic Efficiency of Hospitals." JOURNAL OF HUMAN RESOURCES 9 (Winter 1974): 21-32.

3.3 Eilers, Robert D. "The Changing Environment for Blue Shield." MEDICAL CARE 6 (January/February 1968): 55-68.

3.4 ____ . "Post-payment Medical Expense Coverage: A Proposed Salvation for Insured and Insurer." MEDICAL CARE 7 (May/June 1969): 191-208.

2.4 Evans, Robert G. "Supplier-Induced Demand: Some Empirical Evidence and Implications." In THE ECONOMICS OF HEALTH AND MEDICAL CARE, Proceedings of a conference held by the International Economic Association, April 1973, Tokyo, edited by Mark Perlman, pp. 162-73. New York: John Wiley and Sons, 1973.

2.5 Fein, Rashi. THE DOCTOR SHORTAGE: AN ECONOMIC DIAGNOSIS. Washington, D.C.: Brookings Institution, 1967. 199 p.

_.61 ____ . ECONOMICS OF MENTAL ILLNESS. Monograph Series no. 2. A Report to the Joint Commission on Mental Illness and Health. New York: Basic Books, 1958. 164 p.

*4.3 ____ . "Health Programs and Economic Development." In THE ECONOMICS OF HEALTH AND MEDICAL CARE, Proceedings of a conference held May 1962, Ann Arbor, Mich., edited by S.J. Axelrod, pp. 271-82. Ann Arbor: University of Michigan Press, 1964.

3.5 _____. "Impact of National Health Insurance Plans on Financing." In NATIONAL HEALTH INSURANCE, Proceedings of the conference on National Health Insurance, held November 1970, at University of Pennsylvania, edited by Robert D. Eilers and Sue S. Moyerman, pp. 75-102. Homewood, Ill.: Richard D. Irwin, 1971.

G.15 _____. "Medical Care Needs in the Coming Decade." BULLETIN OF THE NEW YORK ACADEMY OF MEDICINE 45 (October 1969): 255-70.

G.16 _____. "On Achieving Access and Equity in Health Care." MILBANK MEMORIAL FUND QUARTERLY 50 (October 1972): 157-90.

G.17 Fein, Rashi, and Weber, Gerald I. FINANCING MEDICAL EDUCATION, AN ANALYSIS OF ALTERNATIVE POLICIES AND MECHANISMS. New York: McGraw-Hill Book Co., for the Carnegie Commission on Higher Education and the Commonwealth Fund, 1971. 279 p.

*_.62 Feldstein, Martin S. "An Aggregate Planning Model of the Health Care Sector." MEDICAL CARE 5 (November/December 1967): 369-81.

3.6 _____. "An Econometric Model of the Medicare System." QUARTERLY JOURNAL OF ECONOMICS 75 (February 1971): 1-20.

*6.3 _____. ECONOMIC ANALYSIS FOR HEALTH SERVICE EFFICIENCY. Chicago: Markham Publishing Co., 1968. 325 p.

*_.64 _____. "Health Sector Planning in Developing Countries." ECONOMICA 37 (May 1970): 139-73.

1.18 _____. "Hospital Bed Scarcity: An Analysis of the Effects of Inter-Regional Differences." ECONOMICA 32 (November 1965): 393-409.

1.19 _____. "Hospital Cost Inflation: A Study of Nonprofit Price Dynamics." AMERICAN ECONOMIC REVIEW 61 (December 1971): 853-72.

2.6 _____. "The Rising Price of Physicians' Services." REVIEW OF ECONOMICS AND STATISTICS 52 (May 1970): 121-33.

*3.7 _____. "The Welfare Loss of Excess Health Insurance." JOURNAL OF POLITICAL ECONOMY 81 (March/April 1973): 251-80.

G.18 Feldstein, Paul J. "Research on the Demand for Health Services." MILBANK MEMORIAL FUND QUARTERLY 44 (July 1966): 128-62.

G.19 Feldstein, Paul J., and Kelman, Sander. "A Framework for an Econometric Model of the Medical Care Sector." In EMPIRICAL STUDIES IN HEALTH ECONOMICS, edited by Herbert Klarman, pp. 171-90. Baltimore: Johns Hopkins Press, 1970.

3.8 Friedman, Bernard. "Consumer Response to Incentives under Alternative Health Insurance Programs." INQUIRY 10 (September 1973): 31-35.

G.20 Fuchs, Victor R. "The Contribution of Health Services to the American Economy." MILBANK MEMORIAL FUND QUARTERLY 44 (October 1966): 65-101.

G.21 _____. "The Growing Demand for Medical Care." In ESSAYS IN THE ECONOMICS OF HEALTH AND MEDICAL CARE, edited by V.R. Fuchs, pp. 61-68. New York: National Bureau of Economic Research, 1972.

G.22 _____. "Health Care and the United States Economic System." MILBANK MEMORIAL FUND QUARTERLY 50 (April 1972): 211-37.

3.9 _____. "Impact of National Health Insurance Plans on Costs: A Framework for Determination." In NATIONAL HEALTH INSURANCE, Proceedings of the conference on National Health Insurance held November 1970, University of Pennsylvania, edited by Robert D. Eilers and Sue S. Moyerman, pp. 184-98. Homewood, Ill.: Richard D. Irwin, 1971.

G.23 _____. "Productivity in Services: Three Case Studies." In THE SERVICE ECONOMY, pp. 115-27. New York: National Bureau of Economic Research, 1968.

G.24 _____. "What Kind of System for Health Care?" BULLETIN OF THE NEW YORK ACADEMY OF MEDICINE 45 (March 1969): 255-70.

G.25 _____. WHO SHALL LIVE? HEALTH, ECONOMICS AND SOCIAL CHOICE. New York: Basic Books, 1974. 168 p.

2.7 Fuchs, Victor R., and Kramer, Marcia J. DETERMINANTS OF EXPENDITURES FOR PHYSICIANS' SERVICES IN THE UNITED STATES, 1948-68. National Bureau of Economic Research Occasional Paper 117. Washington, D.C.: Department of Health, Education, and Welfare, Publication (HSM) 73-3013, December 1972. 63 p.

G.26 Fuchs, V[ictor].R.; Rand, Elizabeth; and Garrett, Bonnie. "The Distribution of Earnings in Health and Other Industries." In ESSAYS IN THE ECONOMICS OF HEALTH AND MEDICAL CARE, edited by V.R. Fuchs, pp. 119-31. New York: National Bureau of Economic Research, 1972.

3.10 Garbarino, Joseph W. HEALTH PLANS AND COLLECTIVE BARGAINING. Berkeley and Los Angeles: University of California Press, 1960. 301 p.

M   Ginzberg, Eli. MEN, MONEY, AND MEDICINE. New York: Columbia University Press, 1969. 291 p.

G.27 _____. "The Political Economy of Health." Paper presented to the Committee on Social Policy for Health Care, New York Academy of Medicine, held May 1968 in New York City, 1969.

2.8 Golladay, Fredrick L.; Manser, Marilyn E.; and Smith, Kenneth R. "Scale Economies in the Delivery of Medical Care: A Mixed Integer Programming Analysis of Efficient Manpower Utilization." JOURNAL OF HUMAN RESOURCES 9 (Winter 1974): 50-62.

1.21 Greenfield, Harry I. HOSPITAL EFFICIENCY AND PUBLIC POLICY. New York: Frederick A. Praeger, Publishers, 1973. 80 p.

G.28 Grossman, Michael. THE DEMAND FOR HEALTH: A THEORETICAL AND EMPIRICAL INVESTIGATION. National Bureau of Economic Research Occastional Paper 119. New York: Columbia University Press, 1972. 115 p.

G.29 Hansen, W. Lee. "An Appraisal of Physician Manpower Projections." INQUIRY 7 (March 1970): 102-13.

G.30 _____. "'Shortages' and Investment in Health Manpower." In THE ECONOMICS OF HEALTH AND MEDICAL CARE, Proceedings of a conference held May 1962, Ann Arbor, Mich., edited by S.J. Axelrod, pp. 75-91. Ann Arbor: University of Michigan Press, 1964.

G.31 Harrison, Jeffrey L., and Nash, Kent D. "A New Approach to the Physician Shortage." INQUIRY 9 (March 1972): 34-39.

G.32 Hartwell, R.M. "The Economic History of Medical Care." In THE ECONOMICS OF HEALTH AND MEDICAL CARE, Proceedings of a conference held by the International Economic Association, April 1973, Tokyo, edited by Mark Perlman, pp. 3-20. New York: John Wiley and Sons, 1973.

M   Hauser, M.M., ed. THE ECONOMICS OF MEDICAL CARE. London: George Allen and Unwin, 1972. 334 p.

3.11 Hester, James, and Leveson, Irving. "The Health Insurance Study: A Critical Appraisal." INQUIRY 11 (March 1974): 53-60.

3.12 Hibbard, Thomas H. "Insurance and the Optimal Distribution of Medical Care." WESTERN ECONOMIC JOURNAL 9 (September 1971): 231-41.

1.22 Hill, Daniel B., and Stewart, David A. "Proprietary Hospitals Versus Nonprofit Hospitals: A Matched Sample Analysis in California." BLUE CROSS REPORTS r.s. 9 (March 1973): 10-16.

*3.13 Hill, Daniel B., and Veney, James E. "Kansas Blue Cross/Blue Shield Outpatient Benefits Experiment." MEDICAL CARE 8 (March/April 1970): 143-58.

G.33 Holtmann, A.G. "Prices, Time, and Technology in the Medical Care Market." JOURNAL OF HUMAN RESOURCES 7 (Spring 1972): 179-90.

1.24 Hurd, Richard W. "Equilibrium Vacancies in a Labor Market Dominated by Non-Profit Firms: The 'Shortage' of Nurses." REVIEW OF ECONOMICS AND STATISTICS 55 (May 1973): 234-40.

*1.25 Ingbar, Mary Lee, with Lee, Sidney S. "Economic Analysis as a Tool of Program Evaluation: Costs in a Home Care Program." In THE ECONOMICS OF HEALTH AND MEDICAL CARE, Proceedings of a conference held May 1962, Ann Arbor, Mich., edited by S.J. Axelrod, pp. 173-210. Ann Arbor: University of Michigan Press, 1964.

1.26 Ingbar, Mary L[ee]., and Taylor, Lester D. HOSPITAL COSTS IN MASSACHUSETTS. Cambridge, Mass.: Harvard University Press, 1968. 237 p.

1.27 Jacobs, Philip. "A Survey of Economic Models of Hospitals." INQUIRY 11 (June 1974): 83-97.

G.34 Jeffers, James R.; Bognanno, Mario F.; and Bartlett, John C. "On the Demand Versus Need for Medical Services and the Concept of 'Shortage'." AMERICAN JOURNAL OF PUBLIC HEALTH 61 (January 1971): 46-63.

G.35 Joseph, Hyman. "Empirical Research on the Demand for Health Care." INQUIRY 8 (March 1971): 61-71.

*3.14 _____ . "Hospital Insurance and Moral Hazard." JOURNAL OF HUMAN RESOURCES 7 (Spring 1972): 152-61.

1.29 Joseph, Hyman, and Folland, Sherman. "Uncertainty and Hospital Costs." SOUTHERN ECONOMIC JOURNAL 39 (October 1972): 274-84.

*1.30 Kaitz, Edward M. PRICING POLICY AND COST BEHAVIOR IN THE HOSPITAL INDUSTRY. New York: Frederick A. Praeger, Publishers, 1968. 192 p.

2.9 Kehrer, Barbara H., and Intriligator, Michael D. "Task Delegation in Physician Office Practice." INQUIRY 11 (December 1974): 292-99.

M Kelman, Sander. "Toward the Political Economy of Medical Care." IN-QUIRY 8 (September 1971): 30-38.

*2.10 Kessel, Reuben A. "Price Discrimination in Medicine." JOURNAL OF LAW AND ECONOMICS 1 (October 1958): 20-53.

*1.32 Klarman, Herbert E. "Approaches to Moderating the Increases in Medical Care Costs." MEDICAL CARE 7 (May/June 1969): 175-90.

G.36 _____. "Economic Aspects of Projecting Requirements for Health Man-power." JOURNAL OF HUMAN RESOURCES 4 (Summer 1969): 360-76.

M _____. THE ECONOMICS OF HEALTH. New York: Columbia Univer-sity Press, 1965. 200 p.

*1.33 _____. "Increase in the Cost of Physician and Hospital Services." IN-QUIRY 7 (March 1970): 22-36.

1.34 _____. "The Increased Cost of Hospital Care." In THE ECONOMICS OF HEALTH AND MEDICAL CARE, Proceedings of a conference held May 1962, Ann Arbor, Mich., edited by S.J. Axelrod, pp. 227-54. Ann Arbor: University of Michigan Press, 1964.

5.1 Klarman, H[erbert].E.; Francis, J. O'S.; and Rosenthal, G[erald].D. "Cost Effectiveness Analysis Applied to the Treatment of Chronic Renal Disease." MEDICAL CARE 6 (January/February 1968: 48-54.

6.5 Kleiman, Ephraim. "The Determinants of National Outlay on Health." In THE ECONOMICS OF HEALTH AND MEDICAL CARE, Proceedings of a conference held by the International Economic Association, April 1973, Tokyo, edited by Mark Perlman, pp. 66-81. New York: John Wiley and Sons, 1973.

M Krause, Elliott A. "Health and the Politics of Technology." INQUIRY 8 (September 1971): 51-59.

1.35 Lave, Judith R., and Lave, Lester B. "Estimated Cost Functions for Penn-sylvania Hospitals." INQUIRY 7 (June 1970): 3-14.

*1.36 Lave, Judith R.; Lave, Lester B.; and Silverman, Lester P. "A Proposal for Incentive Reimbursement for Hospitals." MEDICAL CARE 11 (March/April 1973): 70-90.

1.37 Lee, Maw Lin. "A Conspicuous Production Theory of Hospital Behavior." SOUTHERN ECONOMIC JOURNAL 37 (July 1971): 48-58.

1.38 _____. "Theoretical Foundation of Hospital Planning." INQUIRY 11 (December 1974): 276-81.

1.39 Lee, Maw Lin, and Wallace, Richard L. "Problems in Estimating Multi-product Cost Functions: An Application to Hospitals." WESTERN ECONOMIC JOURNAL 11 (September 1973): 350-63.

_.66 Leveson, Irving. "Access to Medical Care: The Queensbridge Experiment." INQUIRY 9 (June 1972): 61-68.

G.37 _____. "Comments on Demand Analysis Papers." In EMPIRICAL STUDIES IN HEALTH ECONOMICS, edited by Herbert Klarman, pp. 165-67. Baltimore: Johns Hopkins Press, 1970.

G.38 _____. "Medical Care Cost Incentives: Some Questions and Approaches for Research." INQUIRY 5 (December 1968): 3-13.

_.67 Liefmann-Keil, Elisabeth. "Consumer Protection, Incentives, and Externalities in the Drug Market." In THE ECONOMICS OF HEALTH AND MEDICAL CARE, Proceedings of a conference held by the International Economic Association, April 1973, Tokyo, edited by Mark Perlman, pp. 117-29. New York: John Wiley and Sons, 1973.

*G.39 Lindsay, Cotton M. "Medical Care and the Economics of Sharing." ECONOMICA 36 (November 1969): 351-62.

*G.40 _____. "Real Returns to Medical Education." JOURNAL OF HUMAN RESOURCES 7 (Summer 1973): 331-48.

1.40 Long, Millard F. "Efficient Use of Hospitals." In THE ECONOMICS OF HEALTH AND MEDICAL CARE, Proceedings of a conference held May 1962, Ann Arbor, Mich., edited by S.J. Axelrod, pp. 211-26. Ann Arbor: University of Michigan Press, 1964.

3.17 MacIntyre, Duncan M. "Pricing Health Insurance." In THE ECONOMICS OF HEALTH AND MEDICAL CARE, Proceedings of a conference held May 1962, Ann Arbor, Mich., edited by S.J. Axelrod, pp. 148-69. Ann Arbor: University of Michigan Press, 1964.

1.41 Mann, Judith K., and Yett, Donald E. "The Analysis of Hospital Costs: A Review Article." JOURNAL OF BUSINESS 41 (January 1968): 191-202.

2.14 Masson, Robert T., and Wu, S. "Price Discrimination for Physicians' Services." JOURNAL OF HUMAN RESOURCES 9 (Winter 1974): 63-79.

*5.2 McCaffree, Kenneth M. "The Economic Basis for the Development of Community Mental Health Programs." MEDICAL CARE 6 (July/August 1968): 286-99.

1.43 McKersie, Robert B., and Brown, Montague. "Nonprofessional Hospital Workers and a Union Organizing Drive." QUARTERLY JOURNAL OF ECONOMICS 77 (August 1963): 372-404.

*2.15 Monsma, George N., Jr. "Marginal Revenue and the Demand for Physicians' Services." In EMPIRICAL STUDIES IN HEALTH ECONOMICS, edited by Herbert Klarman, pp. 145-60. Baltimore: Johns Hopkins Press, 1970.

1.45 Morrill, Richard L., and Earickson, Robert. "Hospital Variation and Patient Travel Distances." INQUIRY 5 (December 1968): 26-34.

3.18 Moyerman, Sue S. "Appendix B: Summaries of National Health Insurance Plans." In NATIONAL HEALTH INSURANCE, Proceedings of the conference on National Health Insurance held November 1970, University of Pennsylvania, edited by Robert D. Eilers and Sue S. Moyerman, pp. 287-333. Homewood, Ill.: Richard D. Irwin, 1971.

1.46 Muller, Charlotte F., and Worthington, Paul. "Factors Entering into Capital Decisions of Hospitals." In EMPIRICAL STUDIES IN HEALTH ECONOMICS, edited by Herbert Klarman, pp. 399-415. Baltimore: Johns Hopkins Press, 1970.

1.47 _____. "The Time Structure of Capital Formation: Design and Construction of Municipal Hospital Projects." INQUIRY 6 (June 1969): 42-52.

G.41 Mushkin, Selma J. "Health as an Investment." JOURNAL OF POLITICAL ECONOMY 70 (Supplement 1962): 129-57.

M _____. "Toward a Definition of Health Economics." PUBLIC HEALTH REPORTS 73 (September 1958): 785-93.

M _____. "Why Health Economics." In THE ECONOMICS OF HEALTH AND MEDICAL CARE, Proceedings of a conference held May 1962, Ann Arbor, Mich., edited by S.J. Axelrod, pp. 3-13. Ann Arbor: University of Michigan Press, 1964.

G.42 Mushkin, Selma J., and Weisbrod, Burton A. "Investment in Health-

Lifetime Health Expenditures on the 1960 Work Force." In THE ECONOM-
ICS OF HEALTH AND MEDICAL CARE, Proceedings of a conference
held May 1962, Ann Arbor, Mich., edited by S.J. Axelrod, pp. 257-
70. Ann Arbor: University of Michigan Press, 1964.

3.19 Newhouse, Joseph P. "A Design for a Health Insurance Experiment."
INQUIRY 11 (March 1974): 5-27.

G.43 _____. "Does an Increase in the Price of a Necessity Reduce Welfare
More than an Increase in the Price of a Luxury?" INQUIRY 9 (June
1972): 77-79.

2.16 _____. "The Economics of Group Practice." JOURNAL OF HUMAN
RESOURCES 8 (Winter 1973): 37-56.

2.17 _____. "A Model of Physician Pricing." SOUTHERN ECONOMIC
JOURNAL 37 (October 1970): 174-83.

1.48 _____. "Toward a Theory of Non-Profit Institutions: An Economic Model of a Hospital." AMERICAN ECONOMIC REVIEW 60 (March 1970):
64-74.

*1.49 Newhouse, Joseph P., and Phelps, Charles E. "Price and Income Elastic-
ities for Medical Care Services." In THE ECONOMICS OF HEALTH
AND MEDICAL CARE, Proceedings of a conference held by the International Economic Association, April 1973, Tokyo, edited by Mark Perlman,
pp. 139-62. New York: John Wiley and Sons, 1973.

*4.5 Paglin, Morton. "Public Health and Development: A New Analytical
Framework." ECONOMICA 41 (November 1974): 432-41.

3.20 Pauly, Mark V. "The Economics of Moral Hazard: Comment." AMERI-
CAN ECONOMIC REVIEW 58 (June 1968): 531-37.

*1.50 _____. "Efficiency, Incentives and Reimbursement for Health Care."
INQUIRY 7 (March 1970): 114-31.

1.51 _____. "Hospital Capital Investment: The Roles of Demand, Profits and
Physicians." JOURNAL OF HUMAN RESOURCES 9 (Winter 1974): 7-20.

G.44 _____. MEDICAL CARE AT PUBLIC EXPENSE: A STUDY IN APPLIED
WELFARE ECONOMICS. New York: Frederick A. Praeger, Publishers,
1971. 160 p.

*1.52 Pauly, Mark V., and Drake, David F. "Effect of Third-Party Methods of Reimbursement on Hospital Performance." In EMPIRICAL STUDIES IN HEALTH ECONOMICS, edited by Herbert Klarman, pp. 297-314. Baltimore: Johns Hopkins Press, 1970.

1.53 Pauly, Mark [V.], and Redisch, Michael. "The Not-For-Profit Hospital as a Physicians' Cooperative." AMERICAN ECONOMIC REVIEW 63 (March 1973): 87-99.

G.45 Perlman, Mark. "Economic History and Health Care in Industrialized Nations." In THE ECONOMICS OF HEALTH AND MEDICAL CARE, Proceedings of a conference held by the International Economic Association, April 1973, Tokyo, edited by Mark Perlman, pp. 21-33. New York: John Wiley and Sons, 1973.

*4.6 _____. "Some Economic Aspects of Public Health Programs in Underdeveloped Areas." In THE ECONOMICS OF HEALTH AND MEDICAL CARE, Proceedings of a conference held May 1962, Ann Arbor, Mich., edited by S.J. Axelrod, pp. 286-99. Ann Arbor: University of Michigan Press, 1964.

4.7 Piore, Nora. "Metropolitan Areas and Public Medical Care." In THE ECONOMICS OF HEALTH AND MEDICAL CARE, Proceedings of a conference held May 1962, Ann Arbor, Mich., edited by S.J. Axelrod, pp. 60-70. Ann Arbor: University of Michigan Press, 1964.

1.54 Rafferty, John [A.]. "Measurement of Hospital Case-Mix: A Note on Alternative Patient Classifications." APPLIED ECONOMICS 4 (December 1972): 301-5.

1.55 _____. "Patterns of Hospital Use: An Analysis of Short-Run Variations." JOURNAL OF POLITICAL ECONOMY 79 (January/February 1971): 154-65.

1.56 Reder, M.W. "Some Problems in the Economics of Hospitals." AMERICAN ECONOMIC REVIEW 55 (May 1965): 472-80.

G.46 _____. "Some Problems in the Measurement of Productivity in the Medical Care Industry." In PRODUCTION AND PRODUCTIVITY IN THE SERVICE INDUSTRIES, edited by Victor R. Fuchs, pp. 95-131. New York: National Bureau of Economic Research, 1969.

1.57 Redisch, Michael. "Hospital Inflationary Mechanisms." Paper read at Western Economics Association Meetings, 10-12 June 1974, Las Vegas, Nevada.

2.20 Reinhardt, U. "A Product Function for Physician Services." REVIEW

OF ECONOMICS AND STATISTICS 54 (February 1972): 55-66.

5.3 Rice, Dorothy P. ESTIMATING THE COST OF ILLNESS. Health Economics Series no. 6. U.S. Department of Health, Education, and Welfare--
Public Health Service Publication no. 947-6. Washington, D.C.: Government Printing Office, 1966. 131 p.

2.21 Rimlinger, Gaston V., and Steele, Henry B. "An Economic Interpretation of the Spatial Distribution of Physicians in the U.S." SOUTHERN
ECONOMIC JOURNAL 30 (July 1963): 1-12.

1.58 Ro, Kong-Kyun. "Incremental Pricing Would Increase Efficiency in Hospitals." INQUIRY 6 (March 1969): 3-18.

1.59 _____. "Interactions among Variables Affecting Hospital Utilization."
HEALTH SERVICES RESEARCH 8 (Winter 1973): 298-308.

1.60 _____. "Patient Characteristics, Hospital Characteristics, and Hospital
Use." In ESSAYS IN THE ECONOMICS OF HEALTH AND MEDICAL
CARE, edited by V.R. Fuchs, pp. 69-96. New York: National Bureau
of Economic Research, 1972.

G.47 Roberts, Markley. "Trends in the Organization of Health Services: The
Private Sector." In THE ECONOMICS OF HEALTH AND MEDICAL CARE,
Proceedings of a conference held May 1962, Ann Arbor, Mich., edited
by S.J. Axelrod, pp. 23-41. Ann Arbor: University of Michigan Press,
1964.

3.22 Robertson, Robert L. "Comparative Medical Care Use Under Prepaid
Group Practice and Free Choice Plans: A Case Study." INQUIRY 9
(September 1972): 70-76.

G.48 _____. "Issues in Measuring the Economic Effects of Personal Health
Services." MEDICAL CARE 5 (November/December 1967): 362-68.

1.61 Rosenthal, Gerald D. THE DEMAND FOR GENERAL HOSPITAL FACILI-
TIES. Hospital Monograph Series no. 14. Chicago: American Hospital
Association, 1964. 101 p.

1.62 _____. "Price Elasticity of Demand for Short-Term General Hospital
Services." In EMPIRICAL STUDIES IN HEALTH ECONOMICS, edited by
Herbert Klarman, pp. 101-17. Baltimore: Johns Hopkins Press, 1970.

3.23 Rosett, R.N., and Huang, Lein-fu. "The Effect of Health Insurance on
the Demand for Medical Care." JOURNAL OF POLITICAL ECONOMY

81 (March/April 1973): 281–305.

1.63 Ruchlin, H.S.; Pointer, D.D.; and Cannedy, L.L. "A Comparison of For-Profit Investor-Owned Chain and Nonprofit Hospitals." INQUIRY 10 (December 1973): 13–23.

2.22 Ruffin, Roy J., and Leigh, Duane E. "Charity, Competition, and the Pricing of Doctors' Services." JOURNAL OF HUMAN RESOURCES 8 (Spring 1973): 212–22.

*1.64 Russell, Louise B. "The Impact of the Extended-Care Facility Benefit on Hospital Use and Reimbursements Under Medicare." JOURNAL OF HUMAN RESOURCES 8 (Winter 1973): 57–72.

1.65 Salkever, David. "A Microeconometric Study of Hospital Cost Inflation." JOURNAL OF POLITICAL ECONOMY 80 (November/December 1972): 1144–66.

5.4 Scheffler, Richard M., and Lipscomb, Joseph. "Alternative Estimations of Population Health Status: An Empirical Example." INQUIRY 11 (September 1974): 220–28.

*1.66 Schneider, J.B. "Measuring, Evaluating and Redesigning Hospital-Physician-Patient Spatial Relationships in Metropolitan Areas." INQUIRY 5 (June 1968): 24–43.

5.5 Scitovsky, Anne A. "Changes in the Costs of Treatment of Selected Illnesses, 1951–65." AMERICAN ECONOMIC REVIEW 57 (December 1967): 1182–95.

5.6 _____. "An Index of the Cost of Medical Care—A Proposed New Approach." In THE ECONOMICS OF HEALTH AND MEDICAL CARE, Proceedings of a conference held May 1962, Ann Arbor, Mich., edited by S.J. Axelrod, pp. 128–42. Ann Arbor: University of Michigan Press, 1964.

G.49 Sgontz, Larry G. "The Economics of Financing Medical Care: A Review of the Literature." INQUIRY 9 (December 1972): 3–19.

4.8 Siebert, Calvin D. "Benefit-Cost Analysis and Public Health Expenditures: A Survey." Bureau of Business and Economic Research, College of Business Administration. Working Paper Series no. 71-12. Iowa City: University of Iowa, June 1971. 51 p.

G.50 Silver, Morris. "An Econometric Analysis of Spatial Variations in Mortality Rates by Race and Sex." In ESSAYS IN THE ECONOMICS OF

HEALTH AND MEDICAL CARE, edited by V.R. Fuchs, pp. 161-227. New York: National Bureau of Economic Research, 1972.

G.51 _____. "An Economic Analysis of Variations in Medical Expenses and Work-Loss Rates." In ESSAYS IN THE ECONOMICS OF HEALTH AND MEDICAL CARE, edited by V.R. Fuchs, pp. 97-118. New York: National Bureau of Economic Research, 1972.

2.24 Smith, Kenneth R.; Miller, Marianne; and Golladay, Fredrick L. "An Analysis of the Optimal use of Inputs in the Production of Medical Services." JOURNAL OF HUMAN RESOURCES 7 (Spring 1972): 208-25.

M Somers, Herman M., and Somers, Anne R. A PROGRAM FOR RESEARCH IN HEALTH ECONOMICS. Health Economics Series no. 7. U.S. Department of Health, Education, and Welfare--Public Health Service Publication no. 947-7. Washington, D.C.: Government Printing Office, 1967. 43 p.

1.67 Stevens, Carl M. "Hospital Market Efficiency: The Anatomy of the Supply Response." In EMPIRICAL STUDIES IN HEALTH ECONOMICS, edited by Herbert Klarman, pp. 229-48. Baltimore: Johns Hopkins Press, 1970.

G.52 Stewart, Charles T., Jr. "Allocation of Resources to Health." JOURNAL OF HUMAN RESOURCES 6 (Winter 1971): 103-22.

*4.9 Vogel, Ronald J., and Morrall, John F. III. "The Impact of Medicaid on State and Local Health and Hospitals Expenditures, with Special Reference to Blacks." JOURNAL OF HUMAN RESOURCES 8 (Spring 1973): 202-11.

G.53 Weisbrod, Burton A. "Collective-Consumption Services of Individual-Consumption Goods." QUARTERLY JOURNAL OF ECONOMICS 77 (August 1964): 471-77.

5.7 _____. "Costs and Benefits of Medical Research: A Case Study of Poliomyelitis." JOURNAL OF POLITICAL ECONOMY 79 (May/June 1971): 527-44.

*4.10 _____. ECONOMICS OF PUBLIC HEALTH. Philadelphia: University of Pennsylvania Press, 1961. 127 p.

*5.9 Weisbrod, B[urton].A.; Andreano, R.L.; Baldwin, R.E.; Epstein, E.H.; and Kelley, A.C. DISEASE AND ECONOMIC DEVELOPMENT, THE IMPACT OF PARASITIC DISEASES IN ST. LUCIA. Madison: University of Wisconsin Press, 1973. 218 p.

3.26 Weiss, Jeffrey H., and Brodsky, Lynda. "An Essay on the National Financing of Health Care." JOURNAL OF HUMAN RESOURCES 7 (Spring 1972): 139-51.

G.54 Whipple, David. "Health Care as a Right: Its Economic Implications." INQUIRY 11 (March 1974): 65-68.

G.55 Wirick, Grover, and Barlow, Robin. "The Economic and Social Determinants of the Demand for Health Services." In THE ECONOMICS OF HEALTH AND MEDICAL CARE, Proceedings of a conference held May 1962, Ann Arbor, Mich., edited by S.J. Axelrod, pp. 95-125. Ann Arbor: University of Michigan Press, 1964.

1.69 Worthington, Paul N. "Capital-Labor Ratios in Short-Term Voluntary Hospitals." INQUIRY 11 (June 1974): 98-111.

G.56 Yett, Donald E. "The Chronic 'Shortage' of Nurses: A Public Policy Dilemma." In EMPIRICAL STUDIES IN HEALTH ECONOMICS, edited by Herbert Klarman, pp. 357-89. Baltimore: Johns Hopkins Press, 1970.

*2.25 Yett, Donald E., and Sloan, Frank A. "Migration Patterns of Recent Medical School Graduates." INQUIRY 11 (June 1974): 125-42.

2.26 Zeckhauser, Richard, and Eliastam, Michael. "The Productivity Potential of the Physician Assistant." JOURNAL OF HUMAN RESOURCES 9 (Winter 1974): 95-116.

Appendix B

SAMPLE OF RELEVANT JOURNALS

American Economic Review

American Journal of Public Health

Applied Economics

Blue Cross Reports

Econometrica

Economica

Economic and Business Bulletin

Economic Journal

Health Information Foundation
Research Series

Health Services Research

Hospital Administration

Hospital Management

Hospitals

Inquiry

Journal of Business

Journal of Economic Theory

Journal of Finance

Journal of Health and Human
Behavior

Journal of Human Resources

Journal of Law and Economics

Journal of Political Economy

Journal of Regional Science

Journal of Risk and Insurance

Kyklos

Medical Care

Medical Economics

Milbank Memorial Fund Quarterly
(new name: Health and Society)

Modern Hospital

Public Health Economics

Public Health Reports

Quarterly Journal of Economics

Review of Economics and Statistics

Review of Economic Studies

Social Security Bulletin

Southern Economic Journal

Western Economic Journal (new
name: Economic Inquiry)

Appendix C
SAMPLE OF DATA SOURCES

American Dental Association (publications)

American Hospital Association (publications)

American Medical Association (publications)

Blue Cross Reports

National Advisory Commission on Health Manpower

National Bureau of Economic Research (publications)

United States Government, Publications of the:

A. Department of Commerce, Bureau of the Census

    A.1 Census of Manufacturers

    A.2 Census of Population

    A.3 Current Population Reports

    A.4 Government Finances

    A.5 Office of Business Economics, Survey of Current Business

    A.6 Statistical Abstract

B. Department of Health, Education, and Welfare

    B.1 Public Health Service (e.g., Vital and Health Statistics)

    B.2 Social Security Administration

C. Department of Labor, Bureau of Labor Statistics

D. Department of the Treasury

    E. National Center for Health Statistics

    F. National Institutes of Health

World Health Organization (publications)

Appendix D

DEVELOPING THE 1975 SYSTEMATIC REFERENCE SET

A partial 1975 reference set is systemized in this appendix. New health and medical economics literature was systematically processed through the following procedure:

I. Journals listed in Appendix B were checked for 1975 contributions by economists.

II. Using the two frameworks set forth in chapter 1, each relevant journal article was categorized according to:

    (a) health/medical sector [Reference Matrix row(s)]
    (b) economic content [Reference Matrix column(s)]

III. This categorized reference set was then ordered alphabetically:

Acton, Jan P. "Nonmonetary Factors in the Demand for Medical Services: Some Empirical Evidence." JOURNAL OF POLITICAL ECONOMY 83 (June 1975): 595-614.

    Matrix Framework   (1): $_C{}^S$

Blair, Roger D.; Ginsburg, Paul B.; and Vogel, Ronald J. "Blue Cross-Blue Shield Administration Costs: A Study of Non-Profit Health Insurers." ECONOMIC INQUIRY 13 (June 1975): 237-51.

    Matrix Framework   (3): $_P{}^S{}_F$

Blair, Roger D.; Jackson, Jerry R.; and Vogel, Ronald J. "Economies of Scale in the Administration of Health Insurance." REVIEW OF ECONOMICS AND STATISTICS 58 (May 1975): 185-89.

    Matrix Framework   (3): $_P{}^S{}_F$

Davis, Karen, and Reynolds, Roger. "Medicare and the Utilization of Health Care Services by the Elderly." JOURNAL OF HUMAN RESOURCES 10 (Summer 1975): 361-77.

    Matrix Framework   (3): $_C{}^S$

Frech, H.E. III, and Ginsburg, P.B. "Imposed Health Insurance in Monopolistic Models: A Theoretical Analysis." ECO-

147

NOMIC INQUIRY 13 (March 1975): 55-70.

     Matrix Framework   (3): $_C{}^S$, $_P{}^S$

Holahan, John. "Physician Availability, Medical Care Reimbursement, and Delivery of Physician Services: Some Evidence from the Medicaid Program." JOURNAL OF HUMAN RESOURCES 10 (Summer 1975): 378-402.

     Matrix Framework   (3)/(2): $_C{}^S$, $_P{}^S{}_{L,F}$

Lave, Judith R.; Lave, Lester B.; and Leinhardt, Samuel. "Medical Manpower Models: Need, Demand and Supply." INQUIRY 12 (June 1975): 97-125.

     Matrix Framework   (2):HK

Link, Charles R., and Landon, John H. "Monopsony and Union Power in the Market for Nurses." SOUTHERN ECONOMIC JOURNAL 41 (April 1975): 649-59.

     Matrix Framework   (1):HK

Luft, Harold S. "The Impact of Poor Health on Earnings." REVIEW OF ECONOMICS AND STATISTICS 57 (February 1975): 43-57.

     Matrix Framework   (G):HK

Mitchell, Bridger M., and Vogel, Ronald J. "Health and Taxes: An Assessment of the Medical Deduction." SOUTHERN ECONOMIC JOURNAL 41 (April 1975): 660-72.

     Matrix Framework   (G): FK

Scheffler, Richard M. "The Pricing Behavior of Medical Groups." HEALTH AND SOCIETY (formerly MILBANK MEMORIAL FUND QUARTERLY) 53 (Spring 1975): 225-40.

     Matrix Framework   (2): $_P{}^S{}_F$

_____. "Further Considerations on the Economics of Group Practice: The Management Input." JOURNAL OF HUMAN RESOURCES 10 (Spring 1975): 258-63.

     Matrix Framework   (2): $_P{}^S{}_{L,F}$

Sloan, Frank A., and Richupan, Somchai. "Short-Run Supply Responses of Professional Nurses: A Microanalysis." JOURNAL OF HUMAN RESOURCES 10 (Spring 1975): 241-57.

     Matrix Framework   (G)/(1): HK

IV. Subsequently, the reference set was subdivided according to the health/medical sectors framework and numerical entry coding was assigned:

This process yields numerically and alphabetically ordered reference sets categorized according to health/medical sector and economic content. As in chapter 1, a summary of the systematic reference process is provided in the form of a reference matrix.

REFERENCE MATRIX
(1975, partial)

Sector	1 Consumption of Services	2	Provision of Services 3 L	4 PK	5 F	6 HK	7 PK	8 FK
(1)	1.1					1.2 1.3		
(2)	2.1		2.1 2.4		2.1 2.3 2.4	2.2		
(3)	3.3 3.4 3.5	3.4	3.5		3.1 3.2 3.5			
(G)						G.1 G.3	G.2	

The product of the updating process outlined above (I–IV) is a systemized refer-ence set. This update or product can be used in either or both of the follow-ing ways: Individual reference sets by year can be generated and maintained, yielding reference matrices for 1975, 1976, etc., or individual reference sets may be integrated into the basic reference set, yielding a continually growing, systemized aggregate reference set. This second option can be achieved through a simple computerized procedure currently being developed by the author.